RODEHEAVER'S

GOSPEL SOLOS
and
DUETS

Compiled by
Y. P. RODEHEAVER

A collection of Gospel Songs
suitable for all Church Services
and Social Gatherings

Price, $1.25 Net

Published by
THE RODEHEAVER COMPANY
28 East Jackson Blvd.   721 Arch Street
CHICAGO   PHILADELPHIA

PRINTED IN THE U. S. A.

Suggestions

❧ ❧

It is impossible to make up a song book of any kind to suit all voices; but in this little collection of gospel solos and duets, you will find many that can be adapted to almost any voice or combination of voices. Any good accompanist can change the key to suit the range of voice.

A number of these selections are not especially arranged for two voices, but most of them can be adapted to make very pleasing and harmonious duets. For example, number 137, "O Love That Will Not Let Me Go," has the regular four part arrangement, but the soprano and tenor parts make a very attractive duet without changing a single note. It can also be sung very satisfactorily by soprano and alto with the alto taking the tenor part, or by two male voices.

The same is true with number 79, "Have Thine Own Way, Lord," except in the first phrase of the last brace (After Thy will), the tenor should sing the alto part an octave higher.

Number 64, "The Old Rugged Cross," is used very successfully by Mr. Rodeheaver and Mrs. Asher, baritone and contralto, but it can also be sung by soprano and alto, soprano and tenor, or baritone and tenor, the tenor singing the alto an octave higher. In some cases, it might be necessary to change the key, if it is too high for the tenor.

By making the same kind of modifications in a number of the other songs, they will make very satisfactory duets.

We thank a number of our singers and evangelists for suggestions regarding this collection, and we are hoping it will be of real service.

THE PUBLISHERS.

1   Tell Me the Story of Jesus.

Fanny J. Crosby.   Jno. R. Sweney.

M. 100 = ♩

1. Tell me the sto-ry of Je-sus, Write on my heart ev-'ry word;
2. Fast-ing a-lone in the des-ert, Tell of the days that are passed,
3. Tell of the cross where they nailed Him, Writh-ing in an-guish and pain;

CHO.—Tell me the sto-ry of Je-sus, Write on my heart ev-'ry word;

FINE.

Tell me the sto-ry most pre-cious, Sweet-est that ev-er was heard.
How for our sins He was tempt-ed, Yet was tri-um-phant at last.
Tell of the grave where they laid Him, Tell how He liv-eth a-gain.

Tell me the sto-ry most pre-cious, Sweet-est that ev-er was heard.

Tell how the an-gels, in cho-rus, Sang as they wel-comed His birth,
Tell of the years of His la-bor, Tell of the sor-row He bore,
Love in that sto-ry so ten-der, Clear-er than ev-er I see;

D.C. for Cho.

"Glo-ry to God in the high-est! Peace and good ti-dings to earth."
He was de-spised and af-flict-ed, Home-less, re-ject-ed and poor.
Stay, let me weep while you whis-per, Love paid the ran-som for me.

2 How You Will Love Him!

COPYRIGHT. 1910. BY HOMER A. RODEHEAVER.

E. E. Rexford.   B. D. Ackley.

1. Ye who wander, of sin grown weary, Lonely and far from the safe home-fold,
2. Come, and coming, find peace and pardon Wait-ing for you at the place of pray'r;
3. You should know of this love so tender, Love that is steadfast, and deep, and true;
4. Come, and find that you cannot fathom Love like Christ's till you taste and see;

Come and learn what the love of Christ is, Love whose gladness can ne'er be told.
Kneel and ask for a soul for-giv-en, Christ is yearn-ing to meet you there.
Come and share in its sweetness with me, Come, and find that my Christ loves you.
Height and depths of the love of Je-sus No man knows till it sets Him free.

CHORUS.

O, how you'll love Him when you know Him! Know the Christ who died to set you free;

to set you free,

On Calv'ry's cross His heart was bro-ken, Bro-ken there for you, for me!

rit.

3   He Knows the Way.

A. H. A.   COPYRIGHT, 1913, BY HOMER A. RODEHEAVER.   A. H. Ackley.

1. There is a Guide that nev-er fal-ters, And when He leads I can-not stray,
2. Oft-times the path grows dim and dreary, The darkness hides the cheer-ing ray,
3. He knows the e - vils that sur-round me, The turnings that would lead a-stray,
4. O heart weighed down with nameless anguish, O guilt-y soul torn with dis-may,

For step by step, He goes be - fore me, And marks my path, He knows the way.
Still I will trust tho' worn and wea - ry, My Sav-ior leads, He knows the way.
No foes of night can ere con-found me, For Je - sus leads, He knows the way.
Thine ev-'ry foe, His pow'r will vanquish, Let Je - sus lead, He knows the way.

CHORUS.

He knows the way that leads to glo-ry; Thy ev -'ry fear He will al - lay,

He knows the way   Thy ev-'ry fear

And bring thee safe at last to heav-en, Let Je-sus lead, He knows the way.

4 Good Night and Good Morning.

Lizzie DeArmond.   Homer A. Rodeheaver.

M. 85 = ♩

1. When comes to the wea - ry a bless - ed re - lease, When up-ward we
2. When fad - eth the day and dark shad-ows draw nigh, With Christ close at
3. When home-lights we see shin - ing bright - ly a - bove, Where we shall be

pass to His king-dom of peace, When free from the woes that on earth we must bear,
hand, it is not death to die; He'll wipe ev-'ry tear, roll a - way ev-'ry care;
soon, thro' His won-der-ful love, We'll praise Him who called us His heav-en to share,

CHORUS.

We'll say "good-night," here, but "good-morn - ing" up there.
We'll say "good-night," here, but "good-morn - ing" up there. Good-morn-ing up there where
We'll say "good-night," here, but "good-morn - ing" up there.

Christ is the Light, Good-morn - ing up there where cometh no night; When we step from this

earth to God's heaven so fair, We'll say "good-night" here, but "good-morn-ing" up there.

5 Love Led Him to Calvary.

Geo. O. Webster.

Chas. H. Gabriel.

1. Love led the Sav - ior, in days long a - go, Down to earth's
2. Love, for a man - ger, a - ban-doned a throne, Seek - ing the
3. See - ing the soul in its in - fi - nite worth, Stoop-ing, in
4. Long-ing, in pit - y, the lost ones to save, Brav-ing the

dark-ness, its sin and its woe; Seek-ing the lost ones, His mer - cy to
sin - ful, the sad and the lone; Yearn-ing to win them and make them His
love, to the low - li - est birth, Seek-ing the lost in the by-ways of
Gar - den, the Cross and the Grave, Seek-ing this on - ly, the sin - ful to

CHORUS. *Faster.*

show, Love led Him to Cal - va - ry. Love led Him to
own, Love led Him to Cal - va - ry.
earth, Love led Him to Cal - va - ry.
save, Love led Him to Cal - va - ry.

Cal - va - ry, Love led Him to Cal - va - ry; Seek - ing the

lost, at the ut - ter-most cost, Love led Him to Cal - va - ry.

6

My Redeemer.

P. P. Bliss.

James McGranahan.

M. 72

1. I will sing of my Re-deem-er, And His won-drous love to me;
2. I will tell the won-drous sto-ry, How my lost es-tate to save,
3. I will praise my dear Re-deem-er, His tri-um-phant pow'r I'll tell,
4. I will sing of my Re-deem-er, And His heav'n-ly love to me;

On the cru-el cross He suf-fered, From the curse to set me free.
In His boundless love and mer-cy, He the ran-som free-ly gave.
How the vic-to-ry He giv-eth O-ver sin, and death, and hell.
He from death to life hath brought me, Son of God with Him to be.

CHORUS.

Sing, oh, sing.......... of my Re-deem-er, With His
Sing, oh, sing of my Re-deem-er, Sing, oh, sing of my Re-deem-er,

blood........ He purchased me,....... On the cross ..... He sealed my
He purchased me, With His blood He purchased me, He sealed my pardon, On the

Repeat pp after last verse.

par-don, Paid the debt........and made me free.........
cross He sealed my pardon, Paid the debt and made me free, and made me free.

Somebody Cares.

Fannie Edna Stafford. COPYRIGHT, 1910. BY HOMER A. RODEHEAVER. Homer Rodeheaver.

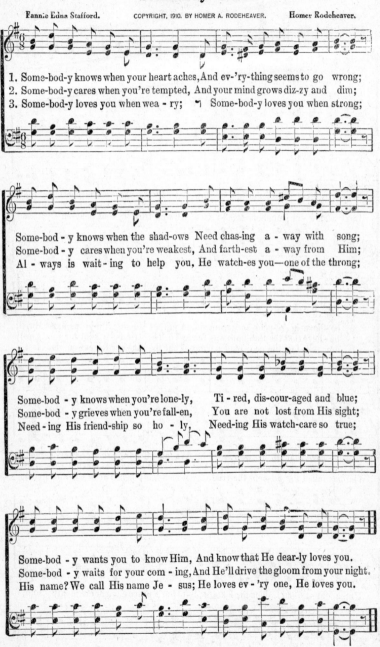

1. Some-bod-y knows when your heart aches, And ev-'ry-thing seems to go wrong;
2. Some-bod-y cares when you're tempted, And your mind grows diz-zy and dim;
3. Some-bod-y loves you when wea - ry; Some-bod-y loves you when strong;

Some-bod - y knows when the shad-ows Need chas-ing a - way with song;
Some-bod - y cares when you're weakest, And farth-est a - way from Him;
Al - ways is wait-ing to help you, He watch-es you—one of the throng;

Some-bod - y knows when you're lone-ly, Ti - red, dis-cour-aged and blue;
Some-bod - y grieves when you're fall-en, You are not lost from His sight;
Need - ing His friend-ship so ho - ly, Need-ing His watch-care so true;

Some-bod - y wants you to know Him, And know that He dear-ly loves you.
Some-bod - y waits for your com - ing, And He'll drive the gloom from your night.
His name? We call His name Je - sus; He loves ev - 'ry one, He loves you.

The Old Fashioned Faith.

8

Rev. N. A. McAulay.

COPYRIGHT, 1911, BY RODEHEAVER-ACKLEY CO.
HOMER A. RODEHEAVER, OWNER.

B. D. Ackley.

M. 56

1. I am somewhat old-fashioned, I know, When it comes to re-lig-ion and God;
2. I be-lieve that the Bi-ble is true, Tho' the crit-ics have torn it a-part,
3. I be-lieve our re-lig-ion must be Not a cloak for our meanness or shame.

Man-y think I am pain-ful-ly slow, Since I walk where my fathers have trod.
All its warnings and mir-a-cles too, I do whol-ly ac-cept with my heart.
But a pow-er from bond-age to free, All who trust in that heav-en-ly name.

I be-lieve in re-pent-ance from sin, And that Je-sus with-in us must dwell;
I be-lieve that the Sab-bath was made To be sa-cred-ly kept for the Lord;
I am tell-ing the peo-ple each day, That the sin-ner for-ev-er is lost,

I be-lieve that if heav-en we win, We must flee from the ter-rors of hell.
And when bro-ken for pleas-ure or trade, We shall miss the e-ter-nal re-ward.
Who has failed to ac-cept the true way Which was o-pened at in-fi-nite cost.

CHORUS.

I'm a lit-tle old fashioned, I know; But God's peace has a home in my soul,

The Old Fashioned Faith.

And I'll praise Him wher-ev-er I go, For cleans - ing and mak-ing me whole.

9

Open My Eyes, That I May See.

C. H. S.   Chas. H. Scott.

1. O - pen my eyes, that I may see Glimpses of truth Thou hast for me;
2. O - pen my ears, that I may hear Voic-es of truth Thou send-est clear;
3. O - pen my mouth, and let me bear Glad-ly the warm truth ev-'ry-where;

Place in my hands the won-der-ful key That shall un-clasp, and set me free.
And while the wave-notes fall on my ear, Ev-'ry-thing false will dis - ap-pear.
O - pen my heart, and let me pre-pare, Love with Thy children thus to share.

CHORUS.

Si-lent-ly now I wait for Thee, Read-y, my God, Thy will to see;

O - pen my { eyes, ears, heart, } il-lum - ine me, Spir - it di - vine!

Saved by Grace.

Fanny J. Crosby.   Geo. C. Stebbins.

1. Some day the sil - ver cord will break, And I no more as now shall sing;
2. Some day my earth-ly house will fall, I can-not tell how soon 'twill be,
3. Some day when fades the golden sun Be-neath the ros - y-tint - ed west,
4. Some day, till then I'll watch and wait, My lamp all trimm'd and burning bright,

But, O, the joy when I shall wake With-in the pal-ace of the King?
But this I know—my All in All Has now a place in heav'n for me.
My bless-ed Lord shall say, "well done!" And I shall en - ter in - to rest.
That when my Sav - ior ope's the gate, My soul to Him may take its flight.

CHORUS.

And I shall see Him face to face, And tell the
shall see   to face,

sto - ry—Saved by grace; And I shall see Him face to
shall see

rit.

face, And tell the sto - ry—Saved by grace.
to face,

11 In The Garden With Jesus.

Wm. C. Poole.

B. D. Ackley.

12 Meet Mother in the Skies.

Arr. by W. S. Nickle

1. In a lone-ly church-yard, ma-ny miles a-way, Lies your dear old
2. Now the old home, va-cant, has no charms for you; One dear form is
3. Now in true re-pent-ance to the Sav-ior flee, He who par-doned

moth-er, 'neath the cold, cold clay; Mem-'ries oft re-turn-ing
ab-sent, moth-er, kind and true; Ev-er-more she dwells where
moth-er, mer-cy has for thee; Now He waits to com-fort,

of her tears and sighs, If you love your moth-er, meet her in the skies.
pleas-ure nev-er dies, If you love your moth-er, meet her in the skies.
He will not de-spise, If you love your moth-er, meet her in the skies.

CHORUS.

Lis-ten to her plead-ing, "Wand'ring boy, come home," Lov-ing-ly en-

treat-ing, do no long-er roam; Let your man-hood wak-en,

Meet Mother in the Skies.

heav'nward lift your eyes; If you love your mother, meet her in the skies.

13   I'm On a Shining Pathway.

John Hogarth Lozier.
SOLO OR CHORUS.

1. I am on a shin - ing path-way, A - down life's short-'ning years,
2. My soul hath had its con - flicts With might-y hosts of sin;
3. I am com - ing near the cit - y My Sav-ior's hands have piled,

And my heart hath known its sor - rows, Mine eyes have seen their tears;
With dead - ly foes with-out me, And dead - lier foes with - in;
And I know my Fa - ther's wait-ing To wel - come home His child;

cres.

But I saw those shad - ows flee, And the shin - ing light I see,
But I saw those le - gions flee, And my soul found vic - to - ry,
For un - wor - thy tho' I be, He will find a place for me,

p

While I'm trust-ing in the mer - it Of the Man of Gal - i - lee.
When I trust-ed in the mer - it Of the Man of Gal - i - lee.
For He is the King of Glo - ry— The Man of Gal - i - lee!

14 Have You a Friend Like That?

H. B.   Herbert Buffum.

1. I have a Friend who is al-ways the same, He nev-er changes thro'
2. This Friend knows all of my tri-als and grief, He knows just how to send
3. When oth-er friendships of earth-ly life fail, When fi-ery darts shall my
4. When I shall en-ter the val-ley of death, Loved ones are wait-ing for

sun-shine or rain; One who can share all my sor-row and pain, Oh,
bless-ed re-lief; All of His prom-is-es I can be-lieve, Oh,
spir-it as-sail; He gives me strength o-ver all to pre-vail, Oh,
my lat-est breath; "Fear not for I will be with you" He saith, Oh,

CHORUS.

have you a Friend like that? Have you a Friend like the Sav-ior so

dear? Have you a Friend who is al-ways near? A Friend who in

rit.

sor-rows can com-fort and cheer, Oh! have you a Friend like that?

15 The Lily of the Valley.

English Melody.

1. I have found a friend in Je - sus, He's ev - 'ry-thing to me, He's the
2. He all my griefs has tak - en, and all my sorrows borne; In temp-
3. He will nev-er, nev - er leave me, nor yet for-sake me here, While I

fair-est of ten-thous-and to my soul; The Lil - y of the Val-ley, in
tation He's my strong and mighty tow'r; I have all for Him forsaken, and
live by faith and do His blessed will; A wall of fire about me, I've

D. S.—Lil - y of the Val-ley, the
FINE.

Him a - lone I see All I need to cleanse and make me fully whole.
all my i-dols torn From my heart, and now He keeps me by His pow'r.
nothing now to fear, With His man-na He my hungry soul shall fill.

bright and Morning Star, He's the fair-est of ten-thousand to my soul.

In sor - row he's my com - fort, in troub-le He's my stay,
Tho' all the world for - sake me, and Sa - tan tempt me sore,
Then sweeping up to glo - ry to see His bless - ed face,

D. S.

He tells me ev - 'ry care on Him to roll. He's the
Thro' Je - sus I shall safe - ly reach the goal. He's the
Where riv - ers of de - light shall ev - er roll. He's the

16 My Wonderful Dream.

COPYRIGHT. 1912 BY CHAS. H. GABRIEL.
HOMER A. RODEHEAVER, OWNER.

Jessie Brown Pounds.

Chas. H. Gabriel.

1. There's a dream that I dream, of my Sav-ior di-vine, And I know that my
2. There is sweet com-pen-sa-tion for heart-ache and loss In the hope that is
3. It will still be my stay when the fashions of earth In the mist are dis-

dream will come true; At the morn, in the night, comes the vis-ion of light,
giv-en to me; I shall quickly for-get how the road was be-set,
solv-ing a-way; For the pass-age of death will be on-ly a breath—

CHORUS.

With a prom-ise e-ter-nal-ly new.
When the King in His beau-ty I see. O this won-der-ful dream is a
But a breath, and my dream will come true.

se-cret of grace, And I would that this se-cret you knew;......... For I
that you knew;

dream that at last I shall look on His face, And I know that my dream will come true.

17 Drifting.

COPYRIGHT, 1917, BY HOMER A. RODEHEAVER.
INTERNATIONAL COPYRIGHT SECURED.

E. E. Hewitt.   B. D. Ackley.

DUET.

M. 112 = ♩

1. Drift - ing care-less - ly with the tide, Drift - ing o - ver the wa-ters wide,
2. Drift - ing al - most up - on the bar, Los - ing sight of the Bea-con Star;
3. Drift - ing on, with no shore in view, Think not skies will be al-ways blue;
4. Drift no lon-ger! let Je - sus save, Let Him guide you a-cross the wave,

With no Cap-tain your course to guide, Drift - ing o - ver life's sea.....
From the ha - ven of joy a - far, Drift - ing o - ver life's sea.....
Storm and ship-wreck will come to you, Drift - ing o - ver life's sea.....
Lest you sink in a sin - ner's grave, Drift - ing o - ver life's sea.....

CHORUS

Drift-ing, drift-ing, no port in sight! Drift-ing far from the gos - pel light;

Lest you go down in the storm - y night; Drift - ing o - ver life's sea.

18 Still Undecided.

Ernest G. Wesley. Chas. H. Gabriel.

1. Still un-de-cid-ed, tho' close to life's gate, O why not now
2. Still un-de-cid-ed, why yet still de-lay? All things are now
3. Still un-de-cid-ed! for thee He was slain, And why should His
4. Still un-de-cid-ed! His voice sounds so clear: "Come all ye who
5. Still un-de-cid-ed! O wait not too long; O turn from the

en - ter, al-read-y 'tis late; Je-sus is wait-ing and call-ing for you;
read-y, Love shows you the way, Night fast approaches, the day pass-es by,
suf - f'ring for thee be in vain? Think of the scourging, the spear and the cross!
wea - ry who fal-ter and fear, Free-ly I par-don, and cleanse and receive!"
world and its wild, restless throng; Je-sus now calls you—once more doth He call—

CHORUS.

Chains He will sev-er— all things He can do.
Heed now His plead-ing:—"O why will you die?"
Life He would give you,—all else is but loss. Why not de-cide to-night?
Why not ac-cept Him and on Him be-lieve?
Come while He's wait-ing, and trust Him for all.

1
Why not de-cide to-night? Je-sus is wait-ing and call-ing for thee,

2
Call-ing for thee, call-ing for thee; Call-ing, is call-ing now for thee.

19 The Angels in Heaven Have Changed My Name.

Arr. by J. B. Herbert.

I know I've been changed, (O yes,) I know I've been changed, (O yes,)

I know I've been changed, (O yes,) The an-gels in heav'n have

FINE. SOLO.

changed my name. 1. I told the Lord if He'd take my heart,—
2. 'Way down a-bout the Jor-dan stream,—
3. It makes me hap-py when I sing,—

CHORUS.

SOLO.

The an-gels in heav'n have changed my name,—I would-n't de-sert
The an-gels in heav'n have changed my name,—I heard a cry,
The an-gels in heav'n have changed my name,—To know that I

CHORUS.

D. C.

when the bat-tle got hot; The an-gels in heav'n have changed my name.
"I have been re-deemed," The an-gels in heav'n have changed my name.
have been born a-gain; The an-gels in heav'n have changed my name.

20 Out of Darkness Into Light.

Ida L. Reed. B. D. Ackley.

M. 63 = 𝅗𝅥.

1. Out of the dark-ness, in-to the light, Out of your weak-ness,
2. Out of your sor-row, in-to His joy, Joy that this earth can
3. Lean on His prom-ise, pre-cious and blest, Come un-to Him for

in-to His night, Je-sus is call-ing, call-ing to-day; Why will you
nev-er de-stroy; Why will you turn the Sav-ior a-way, When He so
par-don and rest; Lo! He is call-ing, call-ing you still, Will you not

CHORUS.

turn from His love a-way? List to His plead-ing, ten-der and sweet,
pa-tient-ly waits to-day?
yield to His bless-ed will?

Kneel with your bur-den low at His feet; Long have you grieved Him, your

Sav-ior and King; Now, tho' un-wor-thy, your all to Him bring.

What a Friend Thou Art to Me.

Fanny J. Crosby.

M. 60

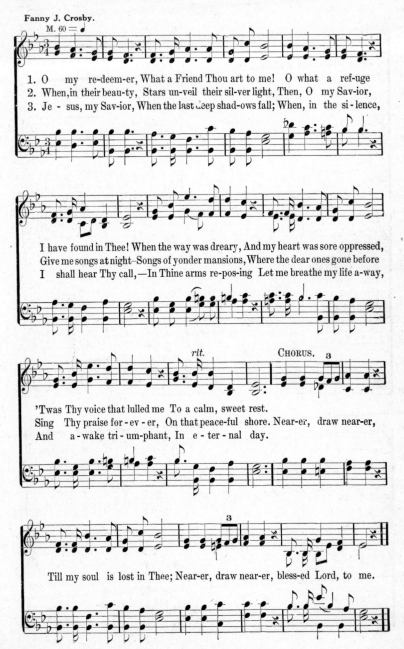

1. O my re-deem-er, What a Friend Thou art to me! O what a ref-uge
2. When, in their beau-ty, Stars un-veil their sil-ver light, Then, O my Sav-ior,
3. Je - sus, my Sav-ior, When the last deep shad-ows fall; When, in the si - lence,

I have found in Thee! When the way was dreary, And my heart was sore oppressed,
Give me songs at night–Songs of yonder mansions, Where the dear ones gone before
I shall hear Thy call,—In Thine arms re-pos-ing Let me breathe my life a-way,

rit.   CHORUS.

'Twas Thy voice that lulled me To a calm, sweet rest.
Sing Thy praise for - ev - er, On that peace-ful shore. Near-er, draw near-er,
And a-wake tri - um-phant, In e - ter - nal day.

Till my soul is lost in Thee; Near-er, draw near-er, bless-ed Lord, to me.

22 Because He Loved Me So.

Rev. A. H. Ackley.

B. D. Ackley.

1. I oft - en stop and won-der why The King of realms be-yond the sky
2. His grace a - lone can fath-om sin, It makes the heart as white as snow;
3. His foot-steps lead me all the way, He guards my path wher-e'er I go,
4. His voice a - lone shall bid me come To heights supreme I long to know,

Should choose to live for me, and die— It was be-cause He loved me so.
He plants the light of love with-in, And all be-cause He loves me so.
He turns earth's darkest night to-day, It is be-cause He loves me so.
Where an - gels sing my welcome home, And all be-cause He loves me so.

CHORUS.

Be - cause He loved me so, Be - cause He loved me so,

He bled and died on Cal - va - ry Be - cause He loved me so.

23 Jesus Leads.

John R. Clements.   Jno. R. Sweney.

M. 76

1. Like a shep-herd, ten-der, true, Je-sus leads, Je-sus leads,
2. All a-long life's rug-ged road, Je-sus leads, Je-sus leads,
3. Thro' the sun-lit ways of life Je-sus leads, Je-sus leads,

Je-sus leads, Je-sus leads.

Dai-ly finds us pas-tures new, Je-sus leads, Je-sus leads;
Till we reach yon blest a-bode, Je-sus leads, Je-sus leads;
Thro' the warrings and the strife Je-sus leads, Je-sus leads;

Je-sus leads, Je-sus leads;

If thick mists are o'er the way, Or the flock 'mid danger feeds,
All the way, before, He's trod, And He now the flock precedes,
When we reach the Jordan's tide, Where life's bound-'ry-line re-cedes,

(1) If thick mists are o'er the way, Or the flock 'mid danger feeds,

rit.

He will watch them lest they stray, Je-sus leads, Je-sus leads.
Safe in-to the folds of God Je-sus leads, Je-sus leads.
He will spread the waves a-side, Je-sus leads, Je-sus leads.

Je-sus leads,

24   Mother's Prayers Have Followed Me.

COPYRIGHT. 1912. BY B. D. ACKLEY.
HOMER A. RODEHEAVER, OWNER.

Lizzie DeArmond.   B. D. Ackley.

1. I grieved my Lord from day to day, I scorned His love so full and
free, And tho' I wandered far away, My mother's pray'rs have followed me.

2. O'er desert wild, o'er mountain high A wanderer I chose to
be, A wretched soul condemned to die, Still mother's pray'rs have followed me.

3. He turned my darkness into light, This blessed Christ of Calvary,
I'll praise His name both day and night, That mother's pray'rs have followed me.

CHORUS.

I'm coming home, I'm coming home, To live my wasted life anew, For mother's pray'rs have followed me, Have followed me the whole world thro'.

25 Where the Gates Swing Outward Never.

C. H. G.

Chas. H. Gabriel.

M. 92 =

1. Just a few more days to be filled with praise, And to tell the
2. Just a few more years with their toil and tears, And the jour-ney
3. Tho' the hills be steep and the val-leys deep, With no flow'rs my
4. What a joy 'twill be when I wake to see Him for whom my

old, old sto-ry; Then, when twi-light falls, and my Sav-ior calls,
will be end-ed; Then I'll be with Him, where the tide of time
way a-dorn-ing; Tho' the night be lone and my rest a stone,
heart is burn-ing! Nev-er-more to sigh, nev-er-more to die—

CHORUS.

I shall go to Him in glo-ry.
With e-ter-ni-ty is blend-ed. I'll ex-change my cross for a
Joy a-waits me in the morn-ing.
For that day my heart is yearn-ing.

star-ry crown, Where the gates swing outward nev-er; At His feet I'll

lay ev-'ry bur-den down, And with Je-sus reign for-ev-er.

26 My Lord and I.

Mrs. L. Shorey.

Joseph D. Little.

1. I have a Friend so pre - cious, So ver - y dear to me,
2. He knows how much I love Him, He knows I love Him well;
3. I tell Him all my sor - rows, I tell Him all my joys,
4. He knows how I am long - ing Some wea - ry soul to win,

He loves me with a ten - der love, He loves so faith-ful - ly,
But with what love He lov - eth me My tongue can nev - er tell;
I tell Him all that pleas - es me, I tell Him what an - noys;
And so He bids me go and speak A lov - ing word for Him;

I could not live a - part from Him, I love to feel Him nigh,
It is an ev - er - last - ing love, In ev - er rich sup - ply,
He tells me what I ought to do, He tells me what to try;
He bids me tell His won - drous love, And why He came to die;

rit.

And so we dwell to - geth - er, My Lord and I.
And so we love each oth - er, My Lord and I.
And so we ⌣ к to - geth - er, My Lord and I.
And so we work to - geth - er, My Lord and I.

The End of the Road.

Dedicated to Evangelist Harry W. Vom Bruch

Lizzie DeArmond.   **Elton M. Roth.**

M. 108 = ♩

1. When I come to the end of the long, long road, The shad-ows will
2. Looking back o'er the years that were hard and drear, The hand of the
3. When I come to the end of the long, long road, And tri - als will

flee a - way, And I'll stand in the glo - ri - ous light of God,
will flee a - way,
Christ I'll see; While my heart will go forth with a song of praise,
the Christ I'll see;
all be past, I shall look in the face of my dear-est Friend,
will all be past,

CHORUS.

Where dwell-eth e - ter - nal day....... When I come to the end, the
Be - cause of His love for me.......
Safe home in His heav'n at last....... When I come to the

end of the road, To the land of e - ter - ni - ty, . When I
To the land of e - ter - ni - ty,

rit.

come to the end of life's long road, The face of my Lord I'll see.

28

Flee as a Bird.

Mary S. D. Dana, 1840.

1. Flee as a bird to the moun - tain, Thou who art wea - ry of
2. He is the boun-ti-ful Giv - - er, Now un - to Him draw
3. He will pro-tect thee for - ev - - er, Wipe ev - 'ry fall - ing

sin;........ Go to the clear flowing foun - tain, Where you may wash and be
near,....... Peace then shall flow as a riv - - er, Thou shalt be saved from thy
tear;........ He will forsake thee, oh, nev - - er, Sheltered so ten-der-ly

clean; Fly, for th' aveng-er is near...... thee, Call, and the
fear. Hark! 'tis thy Sav - ior call - - ing, Haste, for the
there! Haste, then, the hours are fly - - ing, Spend not the

Sav - ior will hear thee, He on His bo-som will bear thee; Oh,
twi - light is fall - ing, Flee, for the night is ap-pall - ing, And
mo - ments in sigh - ing, Cease from your sorrow and cry - ing, The

thou who art wea - ry of sin, Oh, thou who art wea - ry of sin.
thou shalt be saved from thy fear, And thou shalt be saved from thy fear.
Sav - ior will wipe ev - 'ry tear, The Sav - ior will wipe ev - 'ry tear.

29 Jesus, The Savior Of Men.

Mattie B. Shannon.   **B. D. Ackley.**

DUET.

1. How sweet the song with-in my heart, Je-sus, the Sav-ior of men;
2. A sac-ri-fice He died for all, Je-sus, the Sav-ior of men!
3. His mer-cy like a riv-er flows, Je-sus, the Sav-ior of men!
4. No oth-er One can save the soul, Je-sus, the Sav-ior of men!

No oth-er theme can peace im-part, Je-sus, the Sav-ior of men.
His love redeemed us from the fall, Je-sus, the Sav-ior of men.
His wondrous grace the sin-ner knows, Je-sus, the Sav-ior of men.
His pre-cious blood can make us whole, Je-sus, the Sav-ior of men.

CHORUS.

Oh, won-der-ful, won-der-ful sto-ry! We'll sing it a-gain and a-gain;

We'll pub-lish His ex-cel-lent glo-ry, Je-sus, the Sav-ior of men.

30 'Tis Jesus!

Rev. J. Wilbur Chapman.

Robert Harkness.

DUET. M. 104 = ♩

1. I know of a world that is sunk in shame, Where hearts oft faint and
2. I know of a Book, A mar-vel-ous Book, With a message for all who
3. I know of a Home In Im-man-u-el's land, Where hearts ne'er faint nor
4. I know of a Day, A glo-ri-ous Day, When He will come a-

tire; But I know of a Name, A pre-cious Name, That can set that
hear; And the same dear Name, His wonderful Name, Il-lu-mines its
tire; And His marvelous Name, His own dear Name, In-spires the
gain; Then crown Him King, His prais-es sing When He be-

world on fire: Its sound is sweet, Its let-ters flame.
pa-ges clear: The Book is His Word, Its mes-sage I've heard.
heav'n-ly choir: Hear the mel-o-dy ring-ing, My own heart sing-ing.
gins His reign. 'Tis the Day of the Lord, fore-told in His Word;

'Tis Jesus.

REFRAIN.

I know of a name, a pre-cious name, 'Tis Je - - - - - sus.
'Tis Je - sus.

31 The Open Door.

Dedicated to Melvin E. Trotter.

F. S. P.   Florence S. Parkhurst.

1. Down at the feet of my Lord, one day, Brok-en and bruis'd and sore,
2. Too wea-ry to en-ter, too worn to pray, I could but lift my eyes
3. "Look at my side, see my hands and feet, My blood from these wounds has flow'd;"

A cap-tive to sin and in deep dis-may, I cried at His o-pen door.
And look in His face as I heard Him say, "Rejoice! I have paid the price."
'Twas love paid the price, paid the price complete, 'Tis love brings you back to God.

CHORUS.

O would you know of this O-pen Door, O would you en-ter, too?

Look then to Je-sus and sin no more; The ran-som was paid for you.

Deliverance Will Come.

"We are journeying unto the place of which the Lord said,
I will give you."—NUM. 10: 26.

J. M. B.

Rev. Jno. B. Matthias, 1836.

1. { I saw a way-worn trav'-ler In tat-tered gar-ments clad,
   His back was la-den heav-y, His strength was al-most gone,

2. { The sum-mer sun was shin-ing, The sweat was on his brow,
   But he kept press-ing on-ward, For he was wend-ing home;

3. { The song-sters in the ar-bor, That stood be-side the way,
   His watch-word be-ing "On-ward!" He stopped his ears and ran,

And struggling up the moun-tain, It seemed that he was sad; }
Yet he shout-ed as he jour-neyed, De-liv-er-ance will come. }

His gar-ments worn and dust-y, His step seemed ver-y slow: }
Still shout-ing as he jour-neyed, De-liv-er-ance will come. }

At-tract-ed his at-ten-tion, In-vit-ing his de-lay: }
Still shout-ing as he jour-neyed, De-liv-er-ance will come. }

CHORUS.

Then palms of vic-to-ry, crowns of glory, Palms of vic-to-ry I shall bear.

4 I saw him in the evening,
  The sun was bending low,
  He'd overtopped the mountain,
  And reached the vale below:
  He saw the golden city,—
  His everlasting home,—
  And shouted loud, Hosanna,
  Deliverance will come!

5 While gazing on that city,
  Just o'er the narrow flood,
  A band of holy angels
  Came from the throne of God:

They bore him on their pinions
Safe o'er the dashing foam;
And joined him in his triumph,—
Deliverance had come!

6 I heard the song of triumph
  They sang upon that shore,
  Saying, Jesus has redeemed us
  To suffer nevermore:
  Then casting his eyes backward
  On the race which he had run,
  He shouted loud, Hosanna,
  Deliverance has come!

33   I Have a Savior.

W. C. Poole.   J. M. Hagan.

M. 63 = ♩.

1. I have a Sav-ior who light-ens my way,   I have a Sav-ior who
2. I have a Sav-ior who al-ways is true,   I have a Sav-ior who
3. I have a Sav-ior wher-ev-er I be,   I have a Sav-ior on
4. I have a Sav-ior who's reigning with-in,   Read-y and anx-ious to

brightens the day,   I have a Sav-ior who hears when I pray,—'Tis
al-ways will do   All He has prom-ised for me and for you,—'Tis
land or on sea,   Car-ing and watch-ing in love o-ver me,—'Tis
help me to win   Vic-to-ry o-ver all e-vil and sin,—'Tis

CHORUS.

Je - sus, the Light of the world. He makes my way light-er, He

makes my day brighter, He walks all life's journey with me;   His pres-ence and
with me;

glo - ry are round me and o'er me, And light-ens the path-way for me.

So May You.

JAMES ROWE.

B. D. ACKLEY.

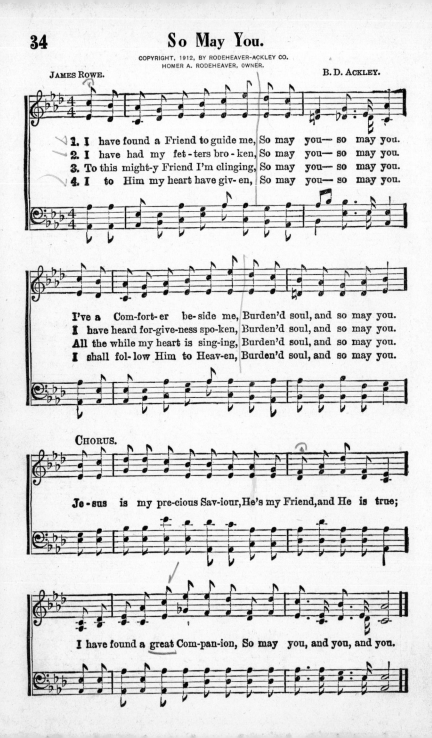

1. I have found a Friend to guide me, So may you— so may you.
2. I have had my fet - ters bro - ken, So may you— so may you.
3. To this might-y Friend I'm cling-ing, So may you— so may you.
4. I to Him my heart have giv - en, So may you— so may you.

I've a Com-fort-er be-side me, Burden'd soul, and so may you.
I have heard for-give-ness spo-ken, Burden'd soul, and so may you.
All the while my heart is sing-ing, Burden'd soul, and so may you.
I shall fol-low Him to Heav-en, Burden'd soul, and so may you.

CHORUS.

Je-sus is my pre-cious Sav-iour, He's my Friend, and He is true;

I have found a great Com-pan-ion, So may you, and you, and you.

35 Looking This Way.

J. W. V.

J. W. VanDeVenter.

DUET.

1. O - ver the riv - er fa - ces I see,   Fair as the morning, looking for me;
2. Fa - ther and mother, safe in the vale,   Watch for the boatman, wait for the sail,
3. Broth-er and sis-ter, gone to that clime,   Wait for the others, com-ing some-time;
4. Sweet lit-tle darling, light of the home, Looking for someone, beckoning " come!"
5. Jesus the Saviour, bright Morning Star,   Look-ing for lost ones stray-ing a - far;

Free from their sorrow, grief and despair, Waiting and watching, pa-tient-ly there.
Bear - ing the loved ones o - ver the tide In - to the har - bor, near to their side.
Safe with the an-gels, whit-er than snow, Watching for dear ones waiting be - low.
Bright as a sunbeam, pure as the dew, Anx-ious-ly look-ing, moth-er, for you.
Hear the glad message; why will you roam ? Je-sus is call-ing, "Sin-ner, come home."

CHORUS.

Looking this way, yes, looking this way; Loved ones are waiting, looking this way;

Fair as the morning, bright as the day, Dear ones in glo - ry look-ing this way.

36 The Master Touched My Heart-Strings.

F. S. P.   Florence S. Parkhurst.

1. My soul is filled with mu - sic, So rich, so full, so free,.... For
2. A fount-ain o-ver-flow - ing With joy, with mys-ter-y;...... This
3. I'm sing-ing of His mer - cy, I'm sing-ing of His love,.... Of

Je-sus touched my heart-strings, And woke a mel - o - dy; How sweetly does it
is my heart since Je-sus Played there His sym-pho-ny; To teach me how to
sac - ri - fice so ho - ly That bro't Him from a-bove; He set the mu - sic

ech - o, And re-ech-o in my heart, Un-til its walls are fal - len,
love Him, And to teach me how to live, He picked the chords so gently
ring - ing, He a-woke my heart one day; And now I'll sing His prais-es

CHORUS.

And I give the world a part.
To teach me how to give. The Mas-ter touched my heart-strings, And bade my
For-ev - er and for aye.

soul, a-wake, To sing His prais - es ev - er; I'm singing for His sake.

37 The Hands of the Savior.

Mattie B. Shannon.

B. D. Ackley.

1. I vi-sion the hands of the Sav-ior, By them were the mul-ti-tudes
2. In pit-y they lift-ed the fall-en, By them were the suf-fer-ing
3. They lead now the way to that Cit-y, "Whose Build-er and Mak-er is

fed; I see them outstretched to the chil-dren, In bless-ing they
healed; They served at the tasks that were hum-ble, The sweet-ness of
God;" They'll nev-er un-clasp till we en-ter, Thro' highways His

CHORUS.

laid on each head,
la-bor re-vealed. Won-der-ful hands, hands of the Sav-ior,
foot-steps have trod.

Nailed for thy sake to the tree;...... Hands that were used in

serv-ice for oth-ers, Hands that will ev-er lead thee.

38 Bridge the Road To Heaven With a Smile.

E. M. P.   E. Margaret Parker.

M. 96 = ♩

1. There is not a care in all the world but smiles can make it light, Then
2. Tho' your path-way seems the roughest, and the rocks and thorns abound, Just
3. Tho' the storm may gath-er o'er you, foes as-sail with-out, with-in, Fear

smile as on your way you go; There is not a cloud so dark but has a
smile a-way the ache and pain; Tho' the ruts are deep and muddy, don't give
not the dan-ger or the strife; If you smile and fight with courage, there is

sil-ver lin-ing bright, And ev-'ry tri-al met is e-ven so.
up and turn a-round, For soon the sun will shine a-way the rain.
One to help you win A crown of joy and ev-er-last-ing life.

CHORUS.

You can bridge the road to heav-en with a sun-ny smile, And its

miles of care and sor-row with a song be-guile; Doubt and fear will not molest;

Bridge the Road To Heaven With a Smile.

You will be su-preme-ly blest If you bridge the road to heaven with a smile.

39 ## Some O' These Days.

ARRANGEMENT COPYRIGHT, 1915. BY C. P. CURRY.

CHORUS.

I'm a-gona to walk on the streets of glo - ry, I'm a-gona to walk on the

streets of glo - ry Some o' these days God knows it, I'm a-gona to walk on the

streets of glo - ry Gona to walk on the streets of glo-ry some o' these days.

1 I'm a-gona sing and shout forever, etc.
2 I'm a-gona down to the river jordon, etc.
3 I'm a-gona meet my sainted mother, etc.
4 I'm a-gona see my blessed Savior, etc.
5 I'm a-gona talk to the Hebrew children, etc.

Over There.

(and JONAH AND THE WHALE.)

Arr. by R. E. W.

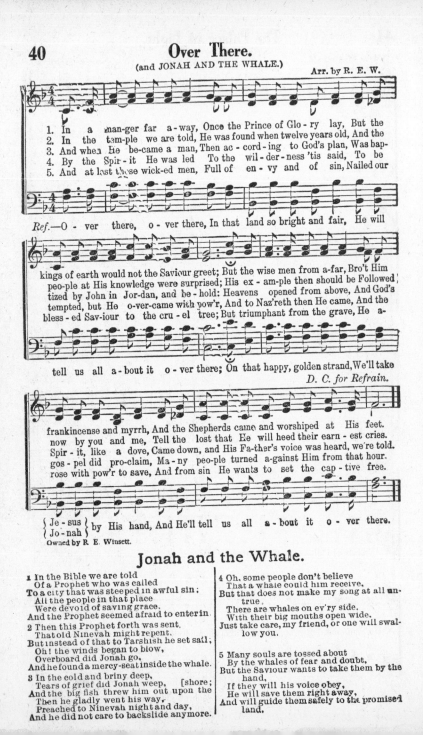

1. In a man-ger far a-way, Once the Prince of Glo-ry lay, But the
2. In the tem-ple we are told, He was found when twelve years old, And the
3. And when He be-came a man, Then ac-cord-ing to God's plan, Was bap-
4. By the Spir-it He was led To the wil-der-ness 'tis said, To be
5. And at last these wick-ed men, Full of en-vy and of sin, Nailed our

Ref.—O - ver there, o - ver there, In that land so bright and fair, He will

kings of earth would not the Saviour greet; But the wise men from a-far, Bro't Him
peo-ple at His knowledge were surprised; His ex - am-ple then should be Followed;
tized by John in Jor-dan, and be-hold: Heavens opened from above, And God's
tempted, but He o-ver-came with pow'r, And to Naz'reth then He came, And the
bless - ed Sav-iour to the cru-el tree; But triumphant from the grave, He a-

tell us all a-bout it o - ver there; On that happy, golden strand, We'll take

D. C. for Refrain.

frankincense and myrrh, And the Shepherds came and worshiped at His feet.
now by you and me, Tell the lost that He will heed their earn - est cries.
Spir - it, like a dove, Came down, and His Fa-ther's voice was heard, we're told.
gos - pel did pro-claim, Ma - ny peo-ple turned a-gainst Him from that hour.
rose with pow'r to save, And from sin He wants to set the cap - tive free.

{ Je - sus }
{ Jo - nah } by His hand, And He'll tell us all a - bout it o - ver there.

Owned by R. E. Winsett.

Jonah and the Whale.

1 In the Bible we are told
   Of a Prophet who was called
To a city that was steeped in awful sin;
   All the people in that place
   Were devoid of saving grace,
And the Prophet seemed afraid to enter in.

2 Then this Prophet forth was sent,
   That old Ninevah might repent,
But instead of that to Tarshish he set sail;
   Oh! the winds began to blow,
   Overboard did Jonah go,
And he found a mercy-seat inside the whale.

3 In the cold and briny deep,
   Tears of grief did Jonah weep, [shore;
And the big fish threw him out upon the
   Then he gladly went his way,
   Preached to Ninevah night and day,
And he did not care to backslide anymore.

4 Oh, some people don't believe
   That a whale could him receive,
But that does not make my song at all un-
   true,
   There are whales on ev'ry side,
   With their big mouths open wide,
Just take care, my friend, or one will swal-
   low you.

5 Many souls are tossed about
   By the whales of fear and doubt,
But the Saviour wants to take them by the
   hand,
   If they will his voice obey,
   He will save them right away,
And will guide them safely to the promised
   land.

41 The Palace of Light.

COPYRIGHT, 1914, BY V. M. HATFIELD.
HOMER A. RODEHEAVER, OWNER.

Victor M. Hatfield.　　　　　　　　　　　Susie E. Hatfield.

M. 138

1. When I've whis-pered fare-well, and for-got-ten my care, When I've
2. When the bat-tle is o-ver, the vic-to-ry won, When the
3. I shall sing a glad song when my eyes shall be-hold The

sung my last car-ol and breathed my last prayer, I'll be met by my
tri-als are end-ed, the jour-ney is done, I shall look on a
cit-y of jas-per with por-tals of gold; Oh, the joy I shall

Sav-ior a-wait-ing me there, In my home in the Pal-ace of Light.
splen-dor more bright than the sun, In my home in the Pal-ace of Light.
know, when the glo-ries un-fold, In my home in the Pal-ace of Light.

CHORUS.

Man-sions of glo-ry, home o-ver there! Re-gion ce-les-tial, ra-diant and fair!

No pain or sor-row, no gloom or night; Beau-ti-ful home-land, Pal-ace of Light.

42 The Good Old-Fashioned Way.

Rev. Johnson Oatman, Jr.   E. O. Excell

1. I am on the Gos-pel highway, Pressing for-ward to the goal, Where for me a rest re-
2. From the snares of sin-ful pleas-ure, Here my feet are al - ways free; Tho' the way may be called
3. Man - y friends have gone before me, They have laid their ar-mor down, With the pil-grims and the
4. Just a few more steps to fol-low, Just a few more days to roam; But the way grows more de-

main-eth In the home-land of the soul: Ev-'ry hour I'm mov-ing on-ward, Not a
nar - row, It is wide e-nough for me; It was wide e-nough for Dan - iel, And for
mar-tyrs Have ob-tained a robe and crown; On this road they fought their battles, Shouting
light-ful As I'm draw-ing near - er home; When the storms of life are o - ver, And the

mo - ment to de - lay; I am go-ing home to glo - ry In the good old-fashioned way.
Da - vid in his day; I am glad that I can fol - low In the good old-fashioned way.
vic - t'ry day by day: I shall o - ver-come and join them In the good old-fashioned way.
clouds have rolled a-- way, I shall find the gates of Heav-en In the good old-fashioned way.

CHORUS or QUARTET.

In the good old - fash-ioned way, In the good old - fash-ioned way,

I am go - ing home to glo - ry In the good old - fash-ioned way.

43 I Want To See Jesus, Don't You?

Ada Blenkhorn. Kem G. Bottorf.

1. There is One loved me so that for me He died, He's my dear, pre-cious
2. When I'm wea-ry and faint He is al-ways near, With His joy He my
3. Ho - ly an-gels keep watch o'er me thro' the night, And each morning He
4. He is fair - er than lil - y or rose to me, And His bless-ings fall
5. There's a place for my soul that He doth pre-pare, And its beau - ty by

Sav - ior so true; On the cross for my sins He was cru - ci - fied:
strength doth re- new; And He comforts my heart, speaking words of cheer:
guards me a - new; In the smile of His love doth my soul de-light:
soft as the dew; O my heart, how it longs His dear face to see:
faith I can view; First of all, when I en - ter that man-sion fair,

CHORUS.

I want to see Je-sus, don't you?.. I want to see Je-sus, don't you?....
don't you? don't you?

My Sav - ior so faith-ful and true;......... When I reach the strand
so faith - ful and true,

of that love-bright land, O I want to see Je - sus, don't you?......
don't you?

44 One Day.

Dr. J. Wilbur Chapman.

Chas. H Marsh.

1. One day when heav - en was fill'd with His prais-es, One day when sin
2. One day they led Him up Cal - va - ry's mountain, One day they nailed
3. One day they left Him a - lone in the gar - den, One day He rest-
4. One day when full - ness of time was fast dawn-ing, One day the stone
5. One day He's com - ing! for Him I am long-ing; One day the skies

was as black as could be, Je - sus came forth to be
Him for me on the tree; Won - der - ful Coun - sel - lor
ed from suf - fer - ing free, An - gels came down then to
moved a - way from the door; Then He a - rose, o - ver
with His glo - ry will shine; Won - der - ful day, my be-

born of a vir - gin, Lived, loved and labored—my Teach-er is He.
they had ac-claim'd Him, Now He is Je - sus—my Je - sus is He.
keep sa - cred vig - il, Weight-ed with sins, my Re-deem - er is He.
death He had conquered, Now He's as-cend-ed, my Lord ev - er-more.
lov - ed ones bring-ing; Hope of the hope-less, this Je - sus is mine.

CHORUS.

Liv - ing He loved me, dy - ing He saved me, Bur-ied He car - ried my

sins far a - way; Ris - ing He jus - ti - fied, free - ly for-

SP 12/14/57

One Day.

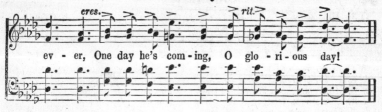

ev - er, One day he's com - ing, O glo - ri - ous day!

45 Refuge.

JOSEPH P. HOLBROOK.

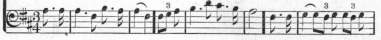

1. Je-sus! Lover of my soul, Let me to Thy bosom fly, While the bil-lows near me

roll, While the tem - pest still is high; Hide me, O my Saviour! hide, Till the

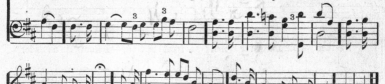

storm of life is past; Safe in-to the ha-ven guide; O receive my soul at last! A - MEN.

2 Other refuge have I none;
   Hangs my helpless soul on Thee;
Leave, ah! leave me not alone,
   Still support and comfort me.
All my trust on Thee is stayed;
   All my help from Thee I bring;
Cover my defenseless head
   With the shadow of Thy wing.

3 Thou, O Christ! art all I want;
   More than all in Thee I find;
Raise the fallen, cheer the faint,
   Heal the sick, and lead the blind.

Just and holy is Thy name,
   I am all unrighteousness;
Vile and full of sin I am,
   Thou art full of truth and grace.

4 Plenteous grace with Thee is found,—
   Grace to pardon all my sin;
Let the healing streams abound,
   Make and keep me pure within;
Thou of Life the Fountain art,
   Freely let me take of Thee;
Spring Thou up within my heart,
   Rise to all eternity.

Charles Wesley.

46 My Father Watches Over Me.

Rev. W. C. Martin.
Chas. H. Gabriel.

Solo, or Unison.

1. I trust in God wher-ev-er I may be,........Up-on the land or
2. He makes the rose an ob--ject of His care,......He guides the ea-gle
3. I trust in God, for, in the li-on's den,...... On bat-tle-field, or
4. The val-ley may be dark, the shadows deep, ... But O, the Shep-herd

on the roll-ing sea, For, come what may, From day to day, My heav'nly
thro' the pathless air, And surely He....Remembers me,— My heav'nly
in the pris-on pen, Thro' praise or blame, Thro' flood or flame, My heav'nly
guards His lonely sheep; And thro' the gloom He'll lead me home, My heav'nly

rit.

CHORUS.

Fa-ther watches o-ver me. I trust in God,— I know He cares for

me,................ On mountain bleak or on the storm-y
He cares for me, On mount-ain bleak or on the

sea;................ Tho' bil-lows roll,............ He keeps my
sea, the storm-y sea; tho' bil-lows roll, He

My Father Watches Over Me.

soul,.......... My heav'n-ly Fa-ther watch-es o - ver me.

keeps my soul,

47 Alone.

B. H. P.

Dueti.

Ben H. Price.

1. It was a - lone the Sav-ior prayed In dark Geth-sem-a - ne;
2. It was a - lone the Sav-ior stood In Pi - late's judgment hall;
3. A - lone up - on the cross He hung That oth - ers He might save;
4. Can you re - ject such matchless love? Can you His claim dis - own?

A - lone He drained the bit - ter cup And suf-fered there for me.
A - lone the crown of thorns He wore For - sak - en thus by all.
For-sak - en then by God and man A - lone, His life He gave.
Come, give your all in grat - i - tude, Nor leave Him thus a - lone.

REFRAIN. *Quartet.*

A - lone, a - lone, He bore it all a - lone; He

it was alone, yes, all a-lone, yes, all a-lone:

ff *dim.* *pp*

gave Him-self to save His own, He suffered, bled and died a - lone, a - lone.

The Prodigal Son.

T. O. Chisholm.   Geo. C. Stebbins.

M. 56 = ♩.

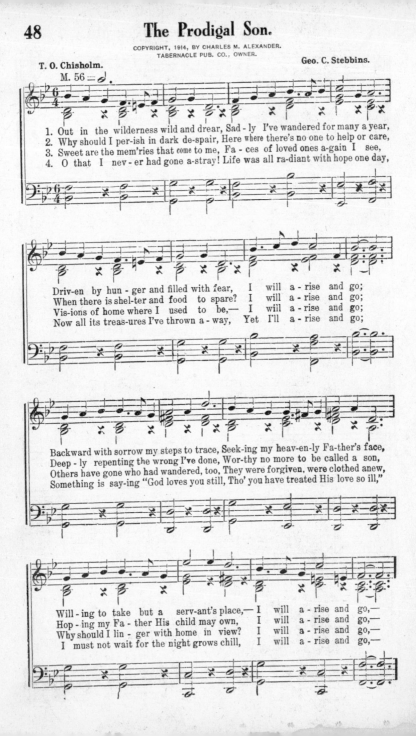

1. Out in the wilderness wild and drear, Sad - ly I've wandered for many a year,
2. Why should I per-ish in dark de-spair, Here where there's no one to help or care,
3. Sweet are the mem'ries that come to me, Fa - ces of loved ones a-gain I see,
4. O that I nev - er had gone a-stray! Life was all ra-diant with hope one day,

Driv-en by hun - ger and filled with fear, I will a - rise and go;
When there is shel-ter and food to spare? I will a - rise and go;
Vis-ions of home where I used to be,— I will a - rise and go;
Now all its treas-ures I've thrown a - way, Yet I'll a - rise and go;

Backward with sorrow my steps to trace, Seek-ing my heav-en-ly Fa-ther's face,
Deep - ly repenting the wrong I've done, Wor-thy no more to be called a son,
Others have gone who had wandered, too, They were forgiven, were clothed anew,
Something is say-ing "God loves you still, Tho' you have treated His love so ill,"

Will - ing to take but a serv-ant's place,— I will a - rise and go,—
Hop - ing my Fa - ther His child may own, I will a - rise and go,—
Why should I lin - ger with home in view? I will a - rise and go,—
I must not wait for the night grows chill, I will a - rise and go,—

The Prodigal Son.

CHORUS.

Back to my Father and home, (and home), Back to my Fa-ther and home,

I will a-rise and go (and go) Back to my Fa-ther and home.

49   Christ is Here.

Rev. A. H. Ackley.   B. B. Ackley.

M. 80 =

1. The wil-der-ness of sin I   roamed,   A des-ert wretched, wild and bare,
2. God gave to me a heav-y   cross,   Too great a cross for me to   bear,
3. I walked within the o - pen tomb,   And gazed upon   its black de-spair,
4. Man's timeless Friend, the changeless One,   I searched and found Him ev'rywhere;

With bro - ken heart and weary tread, ...   My soul with-in   me cold and dead,
Till bowed beneath the pressing load, ...   I stopped to rest   up - on life's road,
To   see   if one there could be found....   To guide thro' that mysterious ground,
The same   sad look up - on His face .....   The same un - dy-ing, boundless grace,

REFRAIN.

1-3. And lo! the Christ was   there,   To answer pray'r,   To answer pray'r.
4. And lo! the Christ is   here,   To answer pray'r,   To answer pray'r.
   And lo!   and lo! the Christ was there,   To answer pray'r,

50 The Palms.

Arr. by C. H. G.

M. 88 = ♩

1. O'er all the way green palms and blossoms gay Are strewn this day in festival
2. His word goes forth, and people by its might Once more their freedom gain from
3. Sing and re-joice, O blest Je-ru-sa-lem, Of all thy songs sing the e-

prep-a-ra-tion, Where Jesus comes, to wipe our tears a-way; E'en now the
deg-ra-da-tion; Hu-man-i-ty doth give to each his right, While those in
man-ci-pa-tion; Thro' bound-less love, the Christ of Beth-le-hem Brings forth the

RESPONSE.

throng to welcome Him prepare. Join, sing His name di-vine,
dark-ness find re-stored the light.
hope to thee for-ev-er-more. Join all, and sing Ho-san-na!

Let ev-'ry voice resound with u-ni-ted ac-cla-ma-tion, Ho-sa- -
Prais'd be the

na! Prais'd be the Lord, Bless Him who cometh to bring us sal-va-tion.
Lord, Ho-san-na!

51 Have You?

Mrs. C. H. M.
Mrs. C. H. Morris.

M. 56 = ♩.

1. I have a great Sav - ior who saves ev - 'ry day, Who guid - eth my
2. A Help - er have I in whom I can con - fide, In dan - gers and
3. I have a great Shepherd who lov - eth His sheep, Who calls them by
4. I've found a great Shel - ter from life's win - try blast, In storm and in

feet lest I wan-der a-stray; Who leads ev-'ry step of life's wea-ry-some way,
tri - als He's close by my side, And keeps me so sweet-ly tho' tempted and tried,
name, and in safety doth keep; They feed in green pastures by still waters deep,
tempest He hold-eth me fast; My hope as an anch-or on Je-sus I've cast,

CHORUS.

I have such a Sav-ior—have you?......
I have such a Help-er—have you?......
I have such a Shepherd—have you?......
I have such a Shelter—have you?......

have you?

I have such a Sav-ior—have

you?   Is my Savior your Savior, too?........ Has He en-tered the
have you?   your Sav-ior, too?

door, to de-part nev-er-more? Is my Sav-ior your Sav-ior too?

52 Sweeter As the Years Go By.

Mrs. C. H. M. COPYRIGHT, 1912, BY CHAS H GABRIEL. Mrs. C. H. Morris.

1. Of Je-sus' love that sought me, When I was lost in sin; Of wondrous
2. He trod in old Ju-de-a Life's pathway long a-go; The peo-ple
3. 'Twas wondrous love which led Him For us to suf-fer loss—To bear, with-

grace that brought me Back to His fold a-gain; Of heights and depths of
thronged about Him, His sav-ing grace to know; He healed the bro-ken-
out a mur-mur, The an-guish of the cross; With saints redeemed in

mer-cy, Far deep-er than the sea, And high-er than the heavens, My
heart-ed, And caused the blind to see; And still His great heart yearneth In
glo-ry, Let us our voi-ces raise, Till heav'n and earth re-ech-o With

CHORUS.

theme shall ev-er be. Sweet-er as the years go by,......
love for e-ven me.
our Re-deem-er's praise. Sweet-er as the years go by, 'Tis

Sweet-er as the years go by; Rich-er, full-er, deep-er,
sweet-er as the years go by;

Sweeter As the Years Go By.

Je - sus' love is sweet - er, Sweet - er as the years go by.

53 The King At the Door.

COPYRIGHT, 1922, BY HOMER A. RODEHEAVER.
INTERNATIONAL COPYRIGHT SECURED.

L. S. L.

Lida Shivers Leech.

DUET. M. 60 = ♩.

1. A Friend who's knocking at thy heart's door, A Friend who oft - en has
2. He knocks so gen - tly with nail-pierced hand; Ah, who His plead-ing could
3. The King of glo - ry now waits out - side, My heart's closed door I will

knocked before; He waits so pa-tient-ly just out-side: It is Christ the Lord.
long withstand! Blest Son of God, mighty Friend of man, Stands at thy heart's door.
o - pen wide; Come in, dear Savior, and e'er a-bide, Be my all in all.

REFRAIN.

'Tis the King at the door, let Him in,.... He will cleanse you from guilt and from
door,.......let Him in, guilt, from

sin;.... Oh, the matchless love of the King above, To be stand-ing there!
guilt and sin;

54 A Heart Like Thine.

J. W. V.   J. W. Van Deventer.

M. 108 = ♩

1. Give me a love that knows no ill, Give me the grace to
2. On-ly a joy, a few brief years, On-ly a dream, a
3. O-pen mine eyes that I may see, Show me the cross of
4. Pil-low my head up-on Thy breast, Shel-ter my soul and

do.... Thy will; Par-don and cleanse this soul of mine,
vale... of tears; Vain is this world I now re-sign,
Cal-va-ry; There may I go and not re-pine,
give.. me rest; Fill me with love as I re-cline,

CHORUS.

Give me a heart like Thine... Come to my soul, bless-ed

Je-sus, Hear me! O Sav-ior di-vine!.....

like Thine......

O-pen the foun-tain and cleanse me, Give me a heart, a heart like Thine.

like Thine......

55   When I Think How He Loved Me.

E. E. Hewitt.

B. D. Ackley.

M. 76 = ♩

1. When I think of how He loved me,   When He left His home on high,
2. When I think of how He loved me,   In   the dark Geth-sem-a-ne,
3. When I think of how He loved me,   "Great-er love" could never be,
4. When I think of how He loved me,   While a sin-ner far a-stray,

To be mocked, despised, for-sak-en,   That my soul should nev-er die:
Of the ag-o-ny He suf-fered,   Wrestling there in prayer for me:
How He bore my sins and sor-rows,   On the cross of Cal-va-ry:
Let my love find sweet ex-pres-sion,   Serv-ing Him from day to day.

CHORUS.

I will praise, for-ev-er praise Him, I   will glo-ri-fy His name;

O   the won-der that He loves me, Pre-cious Je-sus, still the same!

56   He Quiets the Storm.

Jessie P. Tompkins.   B. D. Ackley.

1. The tem-pest was rag-ing on blue Gal-i-lee, And high rose the
2. He woke from His slum-bers and spake to the storm, And, lo! on the
3. O safe is the ves-sel when Je-sus is there, And sure is the

waves of the Pal-es-tine sea, Yet Je-sus was sleep-ing as
wa-ters there fell a great calm; The waves of the deep seemed to
voy-age, if storm-y or fair; There's naught that can harm us when

sweet as a child, Not heed-ing the winds or the wa-ters so wild.
whis-per, " 'Tis He," As safe-ly the ves-sel passed o-ver the sea.
He whis-pers "Peace;" He speaks to the winds and the wild tem-pests cease.

CHORUS.

The bil-lows of sea or of sor-row, Sweet-ly o-bey His will,

And storm-y seas of tri-al,.... List to His "Peace, be still!"

57   Make Me What You Want Me to Be.

W. C. Poole.

COPYRIGHT, 1920, BY HOMER A. RODEHEAVER.
INTERNATIONAL COPYRIGHT SECURED.

Chas. H. Gabriel.

M. 52 = ♩.

1. Make me what you want me to be, O Lord,—I be-long to Thee,..
2. Make me what you want me to be in heart, Saved from ev-'ry sin,....
3. Make me what you want me to be in deed, Serv-ing Thee a-lone,...
4. Make me what you want me to be, to win Souls who are a-stray,..
5. Make me what you want me to be for I Trust a-lone in Thee;..
6. Make me what you want me to be, dear Lord, All for-ev-er Thine,..

In tho't and in pur-pose, in deed and word, Work Thy will in me.....
With-hold-ing from Thee not a sin-gle part, Whol-ly Thine with-in......
And read-y for serv-ice, what-e'er the need—Sav-ior, all Thine own....
To bring others back from the fields of sin, Sav-ior, while I may.....
Thy plan and Thy will as the days go by, Mas-ter, work in me.....
And keep me as prom-ised in Ho-ly Word, By Thy pow'r di-vine....

CHORUS.

Just what you want me to be, dear Lord, Just what you want me to be; All

sin washed a-way—All Thine from to-day, Just what you want me, Lord, make me.

Have Courage, My Boy, To Say No!

H. R. Palmer.

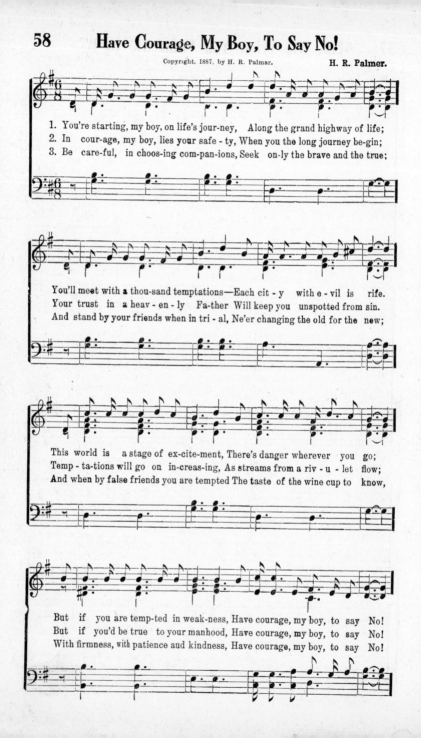

1. You're starting, my boy, on life's jour-ney, Along the grand highway of life;
2. In cour-age, my boy, lies your safe - ty, When you the long journey be-gin;
3. Be care-ful, in choos-ing com-pan-ions, Seek on-ly the brave and the true;

You'll meet with a thou-sand temptations—Each cit - y with e - vil is rife.
Your trust in a heav - en - ly Fa-ther Will keep you unspotted from sin.
And stand by your friends when in tri - al, Ne'er changing the old for the new;

This world is a stage of ex-cite-ment, There's danger wherever you go;
Temp - ta-tions will go on in-creas-ing, As streams from a riv - u - let flow;
And when by false friends you are tempted The taste of the wine cup to know,

But if you are temp-ted in weak-ness, Have courage, my boy, to say No!
But if you'd be true to your manhood, Have courage, my boy, to say No!
With firmness, with patience and kindness, Have courage, my boy, to say No!

Have Courage, My Boy.

CHORUS.

Have courage, my boy, to say No! ... Have courage, my boy, to say No!.....

Have courage, my boy, Have courage, my boy, Have courage, my boy, to say No!

59   Stay Thou Near By.

David J. Beattie.   A. Oliver.

1. Stay Thou near by! Whom have I, Lord, but Thee? Earth's dearest friends may change—their love grow
2. Stay Thou near by! I dare not tread alone The thorny path that once Thy feet didst
3. Stay Thou near by! Life's journey soon will end; Mine eyes are dim, I cannot see my

cold;.... O Savior, Lord, Thou'rt all in all to me,   Thy love's un - told.
tread;... Safe shall I be with Thee to lean upon,   And by Thee led.
way..... O tho't supreme! From earth I shall ascend To bright - er day.

60 Pulling Hard Against The Stream.

Arrangement copyright, 1925, by Homer A. Rodeheaver.

H. Clifton.

M. Hobson.
Arr. by C. H. G.

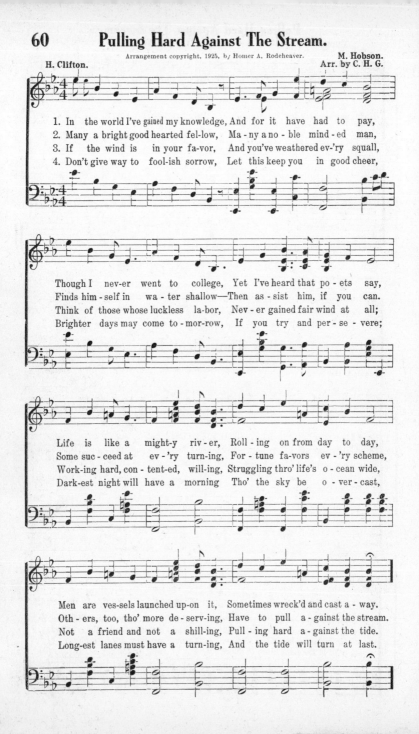

1. In the world I've gained my knowledge, And for it have had to pay,
2. Many a bright good hearted fel-low, Ma-ny a no-ble mind-ed man,
3. If the wind is in your fa-vor, And you've weathered ev-'ry squall,
4. Don't give way to fool-ish sorrow, Let this keep you in good cheer,

Though I nev-er went to college, Yet I've heard that po-ets say,
Finds him-self in wa-ter shallow—Then as-sist him, if you can.
Think of those whose luckless la-bor, Nev-er gained fair wind at all;
Brighter days may come to-mor-row, If you try and per-se-vere;

Life is like a might-y riv-er, Roll-ing on from day to day,
Some suc-ceed at ev-'ry turn-ing, For-tune fa-vors ev-'ry scheme,
Work-ing hard, con-tent-ed, will-ing, Struggling thro' life's o-cean wide,
Dark-est night will have a morning Tho' the sky be o-ver-cast,

Men are ves-sels launched up-on it, Sometimes wreck'd and cast a-way.
Oth-ers, too, tho' more de-serv-ing, Have to pull a-gainst the stream.
Not a friend and not a shill-ing, Pull-ing hard a-gainst the tide.
Long-est lanes must have a turn-ing, And the tide will turn at last.

Pulling Hard Against The Stream.

CHORUS.

So then do your best for one an-oth-er, Mak-ing life a pleasant dream;

Help a worn and wea-ry brother, Pull-ing hard a-gainst the stream.

61   The Sweet Story of Old.

Mrs. Jemima Luke.   J. C. Englebrecht.

M. 50 = ♩.

1. I think when I read that sweet sto-ry of old, When Je-sus was
2. I wish that His hands had been placed on my head, That His arm had been
3. Yet still to His foot-stool in prayer I may go, And ask for a
4. In that beau-ti-ful place He is gone to pre-pare, For all that are

here a-mong men, How He called little children as lambs to His fold, I should
thrown a-round me, And that I might have seen His kind look when He said "Let the
share in His love; And if I now ear-nest-ly seek Him below, I shall
washed and for-giv'n, And man-y dear children are gathering there, "For of

FINE.   CHORUS.   D.S.

like to have been with them then. I should like to have been with them then,
lit-tle ones come un-to Me." "Let the lit-tle ones come un-to Me,"
see Him and hear Him a-bove. I shall see Him and hear Him a-bove,
such is the King-dom of heav'n. "For of such is the King-dom of heav'n,"

62 Going Through the Land.

W. D. Cornell.

Arr. for this book.

1. If a Chris-tian meet a Chris-tian, Go - ing thro' the land,
2. If a Chris-tian gets in troub - le, Go - ing thro' the land,
3. If you meet a soul dis - cour-aged, Go - ing thro' the land,
4. Would you have a home up yon - der, In the bet - ter land?

Just re-mem - ber He's your broth-er, Reach to him your hand;
Don't condemn your weak - er broth-er, Help him all you can;
Show to him God's word of prom - ise, Cheer him all you can;
Do to oth - ers as you'd have them Do to you, my man;

For who can tell but on the mor - row, You and he may stand
For who can tell what great temp-ta-tions Press a - round the man?
For deeds and words in kind - ness giv - en, Mend the brok - en strand;
And when the Mas - ter comes for jew - els, Search-ing thro' the land,

Be - fore the great white throne up yon-der, Help him all you can.
He needs the help of Chris-tian friendship, Give him all you can.
A lit - tle help when one is drown-ing, Oft-en saves the man.
He'll take that wea - ry, faith - ful spir - it Home to Beu - lah land.

63 Glorious City.

K. G. B.

Kem G. Bottorf.

M. 84 = ♩

1. Do you ev-er stop to pon-der On the joys we soon shall see?
2. Can you not foresee its glo-ry— Beau-teous cit-y in the sky?
3. O how glad will be the greet-ing When we reach that home so fair!

Of the home in heav-en yon-der— Stand-ing by the crys-tal sea?
You have oft-en heard the sto-ry— How its pleasures nev-er die.
O how sweet will be the meet-ing With our loved ones o-ver there!

CHORUS.

Glo-rious cit-y..... o-ver there, Where the sun is
Shin-ing cit-y o-ver there,

ev-er shining bright and fair; To that cit-y,....
so bright and fair; shin-ing cit-y,

glo-rious cit-y,.... I am go-ing, and I want to meet you there.
o-ver there,

Above song recorded by Homer Rodeheaver on RAINBOW RECORD—

64 The Old Rugged Cross.

G. B.

Rev. Geo. Bennard.

SOLO AND CHORUS.

1. On a hill far a-way stood an old rug-ged cross, The em-blem of
2. Oh, that old rug-ged cross, so de-spised by the world, Has a wondrous at-
3. In the old rug-ged cross, stained with blood so di-vine, A won-drous
4. To the old rug-ged cross I will ev-er be true, Its shame and re-

suf-f'ring and shame, And I love that old cross where the dear-est and best
trac-tion for me, For the dear Lamb of God left His glo-ry a-bove,
beau-ty I see; For 'twas on that old cross Je-sus suf-fered and died,
proach glad-ly bear; Then He'll call me some day to my home far a-way,

CHORUS.

For a world of lost sin-ners was slain. So I'll cher-ish the old rug-ged
To bear it to dark Cal-va-ry.
To par-don and sanc-ti-fy me.
Where His glo-ry for-ev-er I'll share.

cross, the

cross,...... Till my tro-phies at last I lay down; I will cling to the
old rug-ged cross,

old rug-ged cross,...... And ex-change it some day for a crown.
cross, the old rug-ged cross,

65 All the Way to Calvary.

A. H. A.

Rev. A. H. Ackley.

1. I do not ask for di - a-dem or scep-ter, I do not seek for
2. I know the path He trod is nev - er eas - y, It cost the Son of
3. I can-not turn a - side, for love im-pels me To drink the cup of
4. So trust-ing in His love, I'll toil and suf - fer, Sup-port-ed by His

world-ly joy or fame, I on - ly ask to fol - low my Re-deem-er, And
God His pre-cious blood, It leads on to the cross of name-less an-guish, But
sor - row and of woe; But min-gled with the tears I find the com-fort, The
ev - er-last-ing grace, Un - til at last I rise com-plete, per-fect-ed, Trans-

CHORUS.

tell a - broad the won-ders of His name.
ev - er climb-eth up-ward un - to God.
peace that on - ly Je - sus can be-stow. I will trav-el all the way to
formed to look up - on His bless-ed face.

Cal-va - ry, I will walk the road that Jesus walked for me, I will serve Him to the

end, For He is my dear-est friend, I will trav-el all the way to Cal-va - ry.

66 Oh, Hear Him Calling Thee.

COPYRIGHT, 1916, BY HOMER A. RODEHEAVER
INTERNATIONAL COPYRIGHT SECURED.

Robert Matthews.

ad lib.

1. The voice of Je-sus calls to thee In midst of toil and strife, In ac-cents
2. For-got-ten is the sim-ple trust That childhood bro't to thee, For-got-ten

ten - der of-fers thee The prom-is-es of life. He calls thee from a
now the faith that once Was learned at moth-er's knee; Oh, lost a - while the

world of care, He calls, "Come rest in Me" Yes, 'tis His gen - tle voice I hear
love of Him And oft transgressed His will, Yet He would draw thee back a - gain,

CHORUS. *Slowly.*

Call-ing now to thee. Oh hear Him calling, call-ing thee, The voice of Je - sus
Yes, He loves thee still.

call-ing, Oh hear Him call-ing, calling thee, Oh hear Him call - ing thee.

67   No Room in the Inn.

A. L. Skilton.

E. Grace Updegraff.

1. No beautiful cham-ber, No soft cradle bed,   No place but a man-ger,
2. No sweet con-se-cra-tion, No seeking His part,   No hu-mil-i-a-tion,
3. No one to re-ceive Him, No welcome while here,   No balm to re-lieve Him,

No-where for His head;   No prais-es of glad-ness,   No tho't of their sin,
No place in the heart;   No tho't of the Sav-ior,   No sorrow for sin,
No staff but a spear;   No seeking His treasure,   No weeping for sin,

CHORUS.

No glo-ry but sad-ness, No room in the inn.
No prayer for His fa-vor, No room in the inn.   No room, no room for Jesus, Oh,
No doing His pleas-ure, No room in the inn.

rit.

Lest you should hear at Heaven's gate,
give Him welcome free,   "There is no room for thee."

68. In the Secret of His Presence.

ELLEN LAKSHMI GOREH.   GEO. C. STEBBINS.

1. In the se-cret of His pres-ence how my soul de-lights to hide! Oh, how
2. When my soul is faint and thirst-y, 'neath the shad-ow of His wing There is
3. On-ly this I know: I tell Him all my doubts and griefs and fears:—Oh, how
4. Would you like to know the sweetness of the se-cret of the Lord? Go and

pre-cious are the les-sons which I learn at Je-su's side! Earth-ly cares can
cool and pleas-ant shel-ter, and a fresh and crys-tal spring; And my Sav-ior
pa-tient-ly He lis-tens! and my droop-ing soul He cheers: Do you think He
hide be-neath His shad-ow; this shall then be your re-ward; And whene'er you

nev-er vex me, nei-ther tri-als lay me low; For when Sa-tan comes to
rests be-side me, as we hold com-mun-ion sweet; If I tried, I could not
ne'er re-proves me? What a false friend He would be, If He nev-er, nev-er
leave the si-lence of that hap-py meet-ing-place, You must mind and bear the

rit.

tempt me, to the se-cret place I go, to the se-cret place I go.
ut-ter what He says when thus we meet, what He says when thus we meet.
told me of the sins which He must see, of the sins which He must see!
im-age of the Mas-ter in your face, of the Mas-ter in your face.

A Sinner Made Whole.

COPYRIGHT, 1906, BY CHAS. H. GABRIEL.
COPYRIGHT, 1907, BY E. O. EXCELL

W. M. Lighthall.

Chas. H. Gabriel.

1. There's a song in my heart that my lips can-not sing, 'Tis praise in the
2. I shall stand one day faultless and pure by His throne, Transformed from my
3. All the mu-sic of heav-en, so per-fect and sweet, Will blend with my

high-est to Je-sus, my King; Its mu-sic each moment is thrilling my soul,
im-age conformed to His own; Then I shall find words for the song of my soul,
song and will make it complete; Thro' a-ges un-end-ing the ech-oes will roll,

CHORUS.

For I was a sin-ner, but Christ made me whole, A sin-ner made whole! a

Rit.

sinner made whole! The Savior hath bought me and ransomed my soul! My heart it is

Rit.

singing, the anthem is ringing, For I was a sinner, but Christ made me whole.

R. —2

70 Lord, I Can't Stay Away.

Arr. by J. B. Herbert.

Rather slow and solemn.

Lord, I can't stay a - way, I can't stay a - way, I

rit. e dim. FINE.

can't stay a - way, I can't............ stay a - way.
can't stay a - way.

1. I've got to go to judg-ment to stand my tri - al; I've
2. I've got to go to heav - en to live with Je - sus; I've
3. They're com-in' from the east, from the west they're com - in'; They're

got to go to judg-ment to stand my tri - al; I've
got to go to heav - en to live with Je - sus; I've
com-in' from the north, from the south they're com - in'; They're

D. C.

got to go to judg-ment to stand my tri - al; I can't stay a - way.
got to go to heav - en to live with Je - sus; I can't stay a - way.
com-in' on the rain-bow, and on the clouds, Lord; I can't stay a - way.

He Loves Even Me.

S. L.

Scott Lawrence.

1. When I think of my Sav-ior's great love, In com-ing from Heav-en a-
2. When I think of the thorns on His brow, Seems as if I can see Je-sus
3. When I think how He saves me from sin, Though oft-en un-grate-ful I've

bove, To die on the tree For a sin-ner like me, I am sure that He
now, As He suf-fered for me, That my soul might be free: I am sure that He
been, My vow I re-new, "To be faith-ful and true;" I am sure that He

CHORUS.

loves e-ven me. I am sure that He loves e-ven me, ...

I am sure that He loves e-ven me; . . . . And His love is so

sweet, Makes my joy so complete When I think how He loves e-ven me. . . . .

72 Nobody Like Jesus.

To Homer A. Rodeheaver.

In appreciation of his friendship, spirit, and untiring efforts to do something for others.

Edith L. Mapes.   COPYRIGHT, 1911, BY HOMER A. RODEHEAVER.   Chas. H. Gabriel.

1. Sometimes secret sins creep into my heart,—No-bod-y sees them but Je - sus;
2. Sometimes there are tears that must not be shed, Nobody knows it but Je - sus;
3. Sometimes angry tho'ts are almost expressed, Nobody hears them but Je - sus;
4. Sometimes I am weak, and wander astray, No-bod-y strengthens like Je - sus;
5. Sometimes shut away from all held most dear, Nobody with me but   Je - sus,

But when I confess, He bids them depart,   No-bod-y cleans-es like Je - sus;
In sickness and grief He pil-lows my head,   No-bod-y comforts like Je - sus;
His gentle restraint soon has them suppressed, No-bod-y qui-ets like Je - sus;
He   pa-tient-ly leads me back to the way,   No-bod-y pardons like Je - sus;
My soul nothing lacks, no e - vil I fear,   No-bod-y loves me like Je - sus;

No-bod-y cleans-es like Je - sus,   No-bod-y cleans-es like Je - sus;
No-bod-y comforts like Je - sus,   No-bod-y comforts like Je - sus;
No-bod-y quiets like Je - sus,   No-bod-y qui-ets like Je - sus;
No-bod-y pardons like Je - sus,   No-bod-y pardons like Je - sus;
No-bod-y loves me like Je - sus,   No-bod-y loves me like Je - sus;

But when I confess, He bids them depart;   No-bod-y cleans-es like Je - sus.
In sickness and grief He pil-lows my head,   No-bod-y comforts like Je - sus.
His gentle restraint soon has them suppressed, No-bod-y qui - ets like Je - sus.
He   pa-tient-ly leads me back to the way,   No-bod-y pardons like Je - sus,
My soul nothing lacks, no e - vil I fear,   No-bod-y loves me like Je - sus,

73   O My Soul, Bless Thou Jehovah.

Psalm 103.

From Donizetti,
by J. B. Herbert.

Duet. M. 66 = ♩

1. O my soul, bless thou Je - ho - vah, All with - in me bless His name;
2. He will not for - ev - er chide us, Nor keep an - ger in His mind;
3. Far as east is from west dis - tant, He hath put a - way our sins;

Bless Je - ho - vah, and for - get not All His mer - cies to pro - claim.
Hath not dealt as we of - fend - ed, Nor re - ward - ed as we sinned.
Like the pit - y of a fa - ther, Hath the Lord's com - pas - sion been.

Chorus.

For as high.......... as is the heav - en, Far a -
For as high as is the heav - en,

bove.......... the earth be - low, Ev - er great to them that
Far a - bove the earth be - low,

fear Him Is the mer - cy He will ev - er, ev - er show.

74 I Walk With the King.

James Rowe.

B. D. Ackley.

M. 80 = ♩.

1. In sor-row I wan-dered, my spir-it op-prest, But now I am
2. For years in the fet-ters of sin I was bound, The world could not
3. O soul near de-spair in the low-lands of strife, Look up and let

hap-py—se-cure-ly I rest; From morn-ing till eve-ning glad
help me—no com-fort I found; But now like the birds and the
Je-sus come in-to your life; The joy of sal-va-tion to

car-ols I sing, And this is the rea-son—I walk with the King.
sunbeams of Spring, I'm free and re-joic-ing—I walk with the King.
you He would bring—Come in-to the sun-light and walk with the King.

Chorus.

I walk with the King, hal-le-lu-jah! I walk with the King, praise His name!

No long-er I roam, my soul fac-es home, I walk and I talk with the King.

Home of the Soul.

Mrs. Ellen H. Gates.   BY PERMISSION.   Philip Phillips.

M. 76

1. I will sing you a song of that beau-ti-ful land, The far a-way home
2. O that home of the soul in my visions and dreams, Its bright, jas-per walls
3. That un-chang-a-ble home is for you and for me, Where Je-sus of Naz-
4. O how sweet it will be in that beau-ti-ful land So free from all sor-

of the soul, Where no storms ev-er beat on the glit-ter-ing strand, While the years
I can see; Till I fan-cy but thin-ly the veil in-ter-venes Be-tween
ar-eth stands; The King of all kingdoms for-ev-er is He, And He hold-
row and pain, With songs on our lips and with harps in our hands, To meet

of e-ter-ni-ty roll, While the years of e-ter-ni-ty roll; Where no storms
the fair cit-y and me, Be-tween the fair cit-y and me, Till I fan-
eth our crowns in His hands, And He holdeth our crowns in His hands; The King
one an-oth-er a-gain, To meet one an-oth-er a-gain; With songs

ev-er beat on the glit-ter-ing strand, While the years of e-ter-ni-ty roll.
cy but thin-ly the vail in-ter-venes Be-tween the fair cit-y and me.
of all kingdoms for-ev-er is He, And He holdeth our crowns in His hands.
on our lips and with harps in our hands, To meet one an-oth-er a-gain.

76   How Would It Be With You?

Edith L. Mapes.   Chas. H. Gabriel.

1. If Jesus should come at this moment To catch up with Him in the air
2. If quickly to you came the summons To stand in e-ter-ni-ty now,
3. If Je-sus were standing a-mong us And care-ful-ly searching each heart,

All those who love His ap-pear-ing, For-ev-er to be with Him there, How would He
Where ev'ry tongue shall confess Him, Before whom all nations must bow, Would you be
Bid-ding the ran-somed to en-ter, And saying to oth-ers, de-part; Would you be

find you, I wonder—Watching, waiting, faithful, true? Dear-ly be-lov-ed, con-
read-y to meet Him, In His blood be washed, made new? Dear-ly be-lov-ed, con-
placed at His right hand, Or with those He nev-er knew? Dear-ly be-lov-ed, con-

CHORUS.

sid-er—How would it be with you? How would it be with you, How would it
with you,

be with you? If called face to face now to meet Him, How would it be with you?
with you?

77 Just a Whispered Prayer.

George O. Webster.

Chas. H. Gabriel.

M. 88 = ♩

1. Just a whispered prayer, And the load of care From the burdened heart is
2. Just a whispered prayer, And the load you bear And the darkened path grow
3. Just a whispered prayer, And a Friend is there Who can turn your grief to

lift - ed; And a gleam of light Makes the pathway bright, For the heav-y
light - er; Wheresoe'er thou art, With a lift - ed heart You will find your
glad - ness, Who can fill your days With the notes of praise, Who can give you

CHORUS.

clouds are rift - ed..... Do not trav-el on in dark - ness.... When
skies grow bright-er.... in dark-ness,
song for sad - ness...

you may walk in sun - shine fair;............ You can find the light,
fair, in sun-shine;

And the path-way bright, By the aid of a whis-pered prayer......
by a prayer.

Sowing the Tares.

Unknown.

J. C. Bridges.
Arr. by C. H. G.

1. Sow - ing the tares, when it might have been wheat, Sow - ing of
2. Sow - ing the tares! oh, how dark the black sin! Min - gling a
3. Sow - ing the tares that will bring sor-row down, Rob of its
4. Sow - ing the tares, un - der cov - er of night, Which might have been

mal - ice, spite, and de - ceit; We might have sown ro - ses a
curse with life's sweet-est hymn, And heed - ing no an - guish, no
jew - els life's fair - est crown, And turn - ing to sil - ver the
wheat all gold - en and bright; O heart, turn to God with re-

mid life's sad cares, While we were so cru - el - ly sow - ing the tares.
pit - e - ous pray'rs, While we were so cru - el - ly sow - ing the tares.
once gold - en hairs, Grown whiter as thoughtlessly we sowed the tares.
pentance and pray'rs, And plead for for-give - ness for sow - ing the tares.

Chorus.

Sow - ing the tares, when it might have been wheat, Sow-ing of mal - ice,

Sowing the Tares.

spite, and de - ceit; We might have sown ro-ses a - mid life's sad
cares, But we plead for for - give-ness for sow - ing the tares.

79   Have Thine Own Way, Lord.

A. A. P.

Geo. C. Stebbins.

M. 160. = ♩

1. Have Thine own way, Lord! Have Thine own way!   Thou art the
2. Have Thine own way, Lord! Have Thine own way!   Search me and
3. Have Thine own way, Lord! Have Thine own way!   Wound-ed and
4. Have Thine own way, Lord! Have Thine own way!   Hold o'er my

Pot - ter;   I   am   the   clay.   Mould me and make me
try   me, Mas - ter, to - day!   Whit - er than snow, Lord,
wea - ry,   Help me, I   pray!   Pow - er— all   pow - er—
be - ing   Ab - so - lute sway!   Fill   with Thy Spir - it

Aft - er Thy   will,   While I am   wait - ing Yield-ed and   still.
Wash me just now,   As   in Thy pres - ence Hum-bly I   bow.
Sure - ly is Thine!   Touch me and heal me, Sav-ior di - vine!
Till all shall see   Christ on - ly,   al - ways, Liv-ing in   me!

80 An Old Account Settled.

F. M. G.

F. M. Graham.

M. 80 =

1. There was a time on earth When in the book of heav'n An old account was
2. The   old   account was large, And growing ev-'ry day, For I was al-ways
3. When at the judgment bar   I stand be-fore my King, And He the book will
4. O   sin-ner, seek the Lord, Re-pent of all your sin, For thus He has com-

stand-ing For sins yet un-for-giv'n; My name was at the top, And
sin-ning, And nev-er tried to pay; But when I looked a-head And
o-pen, He can not find a thing; Then will my heart be glad, While
mand-ed, If you would en-ter in; And then if you should live A

man-y things be-low, I went un-to the Keep-er, And settled long a-go.
saw such pain and woe, I said that I would set-tle, And settled long a-go.
tears of joy will flow Be-cause I had it set-tled, And settled long a-go.
hundred years be-low, E'en here you'll not re-gret it, You settled long a-go.

CHORUS.

Long a-go,   Long a-go,   Yes, the old account was
Down on my knees,   I set-tled it all,

set-tled long a-go;   And the record's clear to-day, For He
Hal - le - lu-jah!

An Old Account Settled.

Washed my sins a-way, When the old account was settled long a-go.

81 Dear Little Stranger.

C. H. G.   Copyright, 1928, Renewal, Homer A. Rodeheaver, owner.   Chas. H. Gabriel.

1. Low in a man-ger—dear lit-tle Stran-ger, Je-sus, the won-der-ful
2. An-gels de-scend-ing, o-ver Him bend-ing, Chant-ed a ten-der and
3. Dear lit-tle Stran-ger, born in a man-ger, Mak-er and Monarch, and

Savior, was born; There was none to receive Him, none to believe Him, None but the
si-lent refrain; Then a won-der-ful sto-ry told of His glo-ry, Un-to the
Sav-ior of all; I will love Thee for-ev-er! grieve Thee? no, never! Thou didst for

an-gels were watching that morn.
shepherds on Beth-le-hem's plain.
me make Thy bed in a stall.

CHORUS.

Dear lit-tle Stranger, slept in a man-ger,
But with the poor He slumbered se-cure, The

1

2

No down-y pil-low un-der His head; dear lit-tle Babe in His bed.

82 Confidence.

E. B. Barnes. COPYRIGHT, 1911, BY HOMER A. RODEHEAVER. Homer A. Rodeheaver.

1. Walk Thou with me, nor let my foot-steps stray A-part from Thee, thro'-
2. Thro' wea-ry years my way hath mi-ry been; My bit-ter tears Thy
3. No earth-ly foe can give my spir-it fear; No threat'ning woe can

out life's threat'ning way; Be Thou my guide, the path I can-not see; Close to Thy
pity-ing eye hath seen; My fainting heart hath heard Thy voice divine; My trembling
quail when Thou art near; No tempter's snare can turn my steps aside, For, in Thy

CHORUS.

side, Lord, let me walk with Thee.
hand asks but to rest in Thine. Dear Sav-ior, let me trust my hand in Thine,
care, I'm safe what-e'er be-tide.

And let me know Thy steps are guid-ing mine; Life's changing way is

Rall.

oft-times dark to me, I fear no ill if I may walk with Thee.

83 Jesus, Rose of Sharon.

Ida A. Guirey.   Chas. H. Gabriel.

M. 92 = ♩

1. Je - sus, Rose of Shar - on, bloom with-in my heart; Beau - ties of Thy
2. Je - sus, Rose of Shar - on, sweet - er far to see Than the fair - est
3. Je - sus, Rose of Shar - on, balm for ev - 'ry ill, May Thy ten - der
4. Je - sus, Rose of Shar - on, bloom for - ev - er-more; Be Thy glo - ry

truth and ho - li - ness im - part, That wher-e'er I go my life may
flow'rs of earth could ev - er be, Fill my life com-plete - ly, add-ing
mer - cies heal-ing pow'r dis - til For af - flict-ed souls of wea-ry,
seen on earth from shore to shore, Till the na-tions own Thy sov'reign-

shed a - broad Fra - grance of the knowledge of the love of God.
more each day Of Thy grace di - vine and pu - ri - ty, I pray.
bur - dened men, Giv - ing need - y mor-tals health and hope a - gain.
ty com-plete, Lay their hon - ors down and wor-ship at His feet.

CHORUS.

Je - sus,.............. Rose of Shar - on,..............
Bless-ed Je - sus,   Rose of Shar - on,

Bloom in ra - diance and in love with - in my heart.

84 The Home Over There.

Harriet E. Jones.   B. D. Ackley.

M. 60 = ♩

1. What re-joic-ing there will be When be-yond the si - lent sea We shall
2. What re-joic-ing there will be When the friends of earth we see, Gathered
3. What re-joic-ing there will be Thro' a long e - ter - ni - ty When the

gath - er with our loved ones o - ver there; How the courts of God will ring
near the throne e - ter - nal o - ver there; Clothed in robes of right-eous-ness,
na - tions shall be gathered o - ver there; Giv - ing Je - sus all the praise

As we loud ho-san-nas sing To the bless-ed Lord who gave us entrance there.
Whom the Savior shall confess In the presence of the Fa-ther o - ver there.
For His wondrous works and ways And the mansions waiting for us o - ver there.

CHORUS.

O - ver there, O - ver there, In that home be - yond the

riv - er, bright and fair; Where is nev - er known a night, Where the

The Home Over There.

Sav - ior is the light, While the nev - er - end - ing years are roll - ing on

85   How Tedious and Tasteless.

John Newton.   German.

M. 54 = ♩.

1. How ted - ious and tasteless the hours When Je - sus no lon - ger I see;
2. His name yields the rich - est per - fume, And sweet - er than mu - sic His voice;

Sweet prospects, sweet birds, and sweet flow'rs, Have all lost their sweetness to me;
His   pres - ence dis - pers - es my gloom, And makes all with - in me re - joice;

D.S.-But when I am hap - py in Him, De - cem - ber's as pleas - ant as May.
D.S.-No mor - tal so hap - py as I, My sum - mer would last all the year.

The mid - sum - mer sun shines but dim, The fields strive in vain to look gay;
I should, were He al - ways thus nigh, Have noth - ing to wish or to fear;

3 Content with beholding His face,
My all to His pleasure resigned,
No changes of season or place
Would make any change in my mind:
While blest with a sense of His love,
A palace a toy would appear;
And prisons would palaces prove,
If Jesus would dwell with me there.

4 Dear Lord, if indeed I am Thine,
If Thou art my sun and my song,
Say, why do I languish and pine?
And why are my winters so long?
O drive these dark clouds from the sky,
Thy soul-cheering presence restore;
Or take me to Thee up on high,
Where winter and clouds are no more.

86   In the Dawn of Eternal Day.

E. M. R.

Elton M. Roth.

DUET. Met. 88 = ♩

1. Tho' we jour-ney the path-way that leads thro' the night, And our
2. There are ques-tions and mys-t'ries that oft-en a-rise, As our
3. Tho' the road may seem long, and the jour-ney be hard, And our

feet may be wea-ry and worn; Ev-'ry cloud will be lift-ed and
foot-steps we vain-ly re-trace; But they all shall be quick-ly e-
eyes may be blind-ed with tears, There a-waits for the faith-ful a

all will be bright, In the dawn of that gold-en morn.
rased from our eyes, When we look in His bless-ed face.
glo-rious re-ward, In the home of the end-less years.

CHORUS.

All the tri-als of life will be noth-ing,.... When the

mists have been rolled a-way; And the dark-ness of night Will be

In the Dawn of Eternal Day.

turned in - to light, In the dawn of e - ter - nal day.

87   He Died of A Broken Heart.

T, D.   T. Dennis.

1. Have you read the sto - ry of the Cross, Where Je-sus bled and died;
2. Have you read how they placed the crown of thorns Upon His brow for you,
3. Have you read how He saved the dy - ing thief, When hanging on the tree,
4. Have you read that He looked to Heav'n and said, "'Tis finished?" 'Twas for thee!

Where your debt was paid by His precious blood That fl owed from His wounded side?
When He prayed, "For-give them, oh, for-give; They know not what they do"?
When He looked with plead-ing eyes and said, "Dear Lord, re-mem-ber Me"?
Have you ev - er said, "I thank Thee, Lord, For giving Thy life for me"?

CHORUS.

He died of a bro-ken heart for thee, He died of a bro - ken heart; ....
died, He died of a bro - ken heart;

Oh, wondrous love! it was for thee He died of a bro - ken heart.

88 When I Go Home.

COPYRIGHT, 1913, BY E. O. EXCELL.

Jennie Ree.   Chas. H. Gabriel.

1. A lit - tle while and then the sum - mer Day, When I go Home;
2. Work ceas-es not in sun-shine or in show'r, Till I go Home;
3. All will be well, and all be hap - pi - ness, When I go Home;
4. I'll meet the loved ones I have lost a - while, When I go Home;

'T is lone-some win - ter now, but 't will be May, When I go Home; Be-
But in the still - ness of the twi - light hour, I dream of Home; And
The wan - der - ings all o'er, and lone - li - ness, When I go Home; There
And, best of all, I'll see my Sav - ior smile, When I go Home; Oh,

yond the gloom of moor and fen I see The wel - come warm of
when the night-wind moans a - cross the wold I feel no dread of
will be light at e - ven - tide for me, The light that nev - er
what a joy thro' all e - ter - ni - ty, To sing the praise of

those who wait for me, When I go Home, when I go Home.
dark, or chill of cold— I dream of Home, I dream of Home.
was on land or sea, When I go Home, when I go Home.
Him who died for me, When I go Home, when I go Home.

89 Better Each Day.

Rev. A. H. Ackley.

B. D. Ackley.

1. I love Him each day far bet-ter Than ev-er I've loved Him be-fore; I'm learn-ing the bless-ed se-cret Of trust-ing Him more and more.

2. My joy is a name-less glo-ry, The star of my Hope bright-er grows; The soul of my life is Je-sus, The Conq'ror of all my foes.

3. I hold with Him sweet com-mun-ion, And more of His beau-ty I see; The win-dows of Heav-en o-pen, Re-veal-ing His face to me.

CHORUS.

I love Him each day far bet-ter Than ev-er I've loved Him be-fore; I'm learn-ing the bless-ed se-cret Of trust-ing Him more and more.

The Crown of Thorns.

Isaiah LIII.

John R. Clements.

Marie D. Forrest.

1. De - spised and re - ject-ed; Ac-quaint-ed with grief; In sor - row He
2. O love all sur-pass-ing, A - maz-ing to see; To bear un-com-
3. Like sheep we have wandered; Each turned to his way; The Lord on the
4. O sad Man of Sor-row, So lit - tle esteemed; In an - guish more

suf-fered To bring man re - lief; His path - way was sor - rows, His
plain-ing These sor - rows for me; His path - way was sor - rows, His
Shepherd The bur - dens must lay; His path - way was sor - rows, His
try - ing Than mor - tal has dreamed; His path - way was sor - rows, His

pil - low was thorns, And these make the crown that His fore - head a-

dorns, And these make the crown that His fore - head a - dorns.

91

Will There Be Any Stars?

E. E. Hewitt.   Jno. R. Sweney.

M. 76

1. I am think-ing to-day of that beau-ti-ful land I shall reach when the
2. In the strength of the Lord let me labor and pray, Let me watch as a
3. Oh, what joy it will be when His face I be-hold, Liv-ing gems at His

sun go-eth down; When thro' won-der-ful grace by my Sav-ior I stand,
win-ner of souls; That bright stars may be mine in the glo-ri-ous day,
feet to lay down; It would sweet-en my bliss in the cit-y of gold,

CHORUS.

Will there be a-ny stars in my crown?
When His praise like the sea-billow rolls. Will there be a-ny stars, a-ny
Should there be a-ny stars in my crown.

stars in my crown When at ev'ning the sun go-eth down?...... When I
go-eth down?

wake with the blest In the mansion of rest, Will there be any stars in my crown?...
any stars in my crown?

92 The Lights of Home.

FANNY J. CROSBY. CHAS. H. MARSH.

DUET.

1. O the friends that now are wait-ing, In the cloudless realms of day,
2. They have laid a-side their ar - mor For a robe of spotless white;
3. On those dear fa - mil - iar fa - ces There will be no trace of care;

Who are call - ing me to fol - low Where their steps have led the way;
And with Je - sus they are walk-ing Where the riv - er sparkles bright.
Ev - 'ry sigh was hush'd for-ev - er At the pal - ace gate so fair.

They have laid a-side their ar - mor, And their earth-ly course is run;
We have la-bored here to-geth - er, We have la - bored side by side,
I shall see them, I shall know them, I shall hear their song of love,

They have kept the faith with patience And their crown of life is won.
Just a lit - tle while be- fore me They have cross'd the roll-ing tide.
And we'll all sing hal - le - lu - jah In our Father's house a - bove.

REFRAIN.

They are call - ing, gent-ly call-ing, Sweetly call - ing me to come,

The Lights Of Home.

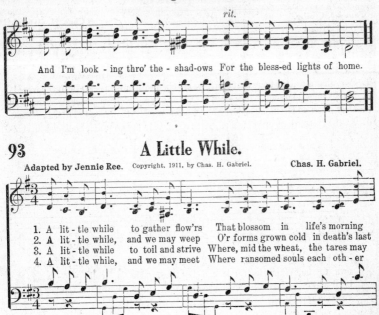

rit.

And I'm look - ing thro' the - shad-ows For the bless-ed lights of home.

93   A Little While.

Adapted by Jennie Ree.   Copyright, 1911, by Chas. H. Gabriel.   **Chas. H. Gabriel.**

1. A lit - tle while   to gather flow'rs   That blossom in   life's morning
2. A lit - tle while,   and we may weep   O'r forms grown cold in death's last
3. A lit - tle while   to toil and strive   Where, mid the wheat, the tares may
4. A lit - tle while,   and we may meet   Where ransomed souls each oth - er

hours;   A lit - tle while   to dream a - way   The glo - ries
sleep;   A lit - tle while   to pray and mourn   Where friends from
thrive;   A lit - tle while—   and then shall I   Be-neath the
greet;   A lit - tle while,   and an - gels fair,   With songs shall

of   the bright spring day,   A lit - tle while,   A lit-tle while.
love's   strong arms are torn,—   A lit - tle while,   A lit-tle while.
droop - ing wil - lows lie—   A lit - tle while,   A lit-tle while.
make   us wel-come there—   A lit - tle while,   A lit-tle while.

94 Calling Thee.

Fanny J. Crosby.

Chas. H. Gabriel.

M. 80 = ♩

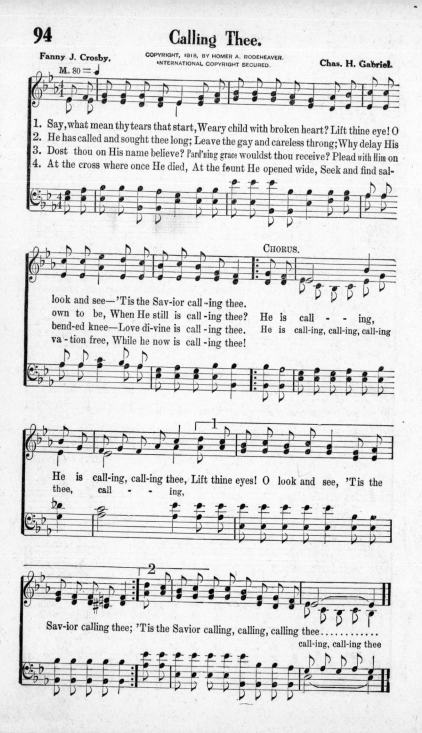

1. Say, what mean thy tears that start, Weary child with broken heart? Lift thine eye! O
2. He has called and sought thee long; Leave the gay and careless throng; Why delay His
3. Dost thou on His name believe? Pard'ning grace wouldst thou receive? Plead with Him on
4. At the cross where once He died, At the fount He opened wide, Seek and find sal-

CHORUS.

look and see—'Tis the Sav-ior call-ing thee.
own to be, When He still is call-ing thee? He is call - - ing,
bend-ed knee—Love di-vine is call-ing thee. He is call-ing, call-ing, call-ing
va-tion free, While he now is call-ing thee!

1

He is call-ing, call-ing thee, Lift thine eyes! O look and see, 'Tis the
thee, call - - ing,

2

Sav-ior calling thee; 'Tis the Savior calling, calling, calling thee............
call-ing, call-ing thee

95 What Would We Do Without the Clouds?

A. H. A.   Rev. A. H. Ackley.

M. 100 = ♩

1. God is good, He sends the rain; For His glo-ry, we should not com-plain;
2. Verdant meadows, fruits and flow'rs, Gath-er beau-ty from the fall-ing show'rs;
3. Cloudless sky makes bar-ren land; Parched and thirsty is the des-ert sand;

What He sends is al-ways best, Stormy clouds and all the rest.........
Clouds are sail-boats from a-bove, La-den with the gifts of love.........
So would life be bar-ren, too, If there were no clouds for you.........

Chorus.

What would we do without the clouds? The clouds bring rain, Scat-ter-ing show'rs of
bless-ing o-ver hill and plain, Bring-ing to us the har-vest of the
gol-den grain; What would we do with-out the clouds? The clouds bring rain.

Christ is All.

W. A. W.

W. A. Williams.

May be sung as a Solo or Chorus.

1. I en-tered once a home of care, For age and pen - u - ry were
2. I stood be - side a dy - ing bed, Where lay a child with ach - ing
3. I saw the mar - tyr at the stake; The flames could not his cour - age
4. I saw the gos - pel her - ald go To Af - ric's sand and Green-land's
5. Then come to Christ, "oh, come to-day!" The Fa-ther, Son and Spir - it

there, Yet peace and joy with - al; I asked the lone - ly moth-er
head, Wait - ing for Je - sus' call; I marked his smile, 'twas sweet as
shake, Nor death his soul ap - pall; I asked him whence his strength was
snow, To save from Sa-tan's thrall; Nor home nor life he count-ed
say, The Bride re - peats the call; For He will cleanse your guilt - y

whence Her help-less wid-ow-hood's de-fence; She told me "Christ was all."
May, And as his spir - it passed a - way, He whis-pered "Christ is all."
giv'n, He looked tri-umph-ant-ly to heav'n, And an-swered "Christ is all."
dear, 'Midst want and per-ils owned no fear, He felt that "Christ is all."
stains, His love will soothe your wea-ry pains, For "Christ is all in all."

CHORUS.

Christ is all, all in all, Yes, Christ is all in all: Yes, Christ is all in all.

The Royal Telephone.

F. M. LEHMAN.
Har. by CLAUDIA F. LEHMAN.

F. M. L.

1. Central's nev-er "bus-y," Al-ways on the line, You may hear from
2. There will be no charg-es, Tel-e-phone is free; It was built for
3. Fail to get the an-swer, Satan's crossed your wire By some strong de-
4. If your line is "grounded," And con-nec-tion true Has been lost with
5. Car-nal com-bi-na-tions Can-not get con-trol Of this line to

heav-en Al-most an-y time. 'Tis a roy-al serv-ice
serv-ice, Just for you and me. There will be no wait-ing
lu-sion, Or some base de-sire. Take a-way ob-struc-tions—
Je-sus, Tell you what to do: Pray'r and faith and promise
glo-ry, Anchored in the soul. Storm and tri-al can-not

FINE.

Free for one and all—When you get in trouble Give this roy-al line a call.
On this roy-al line— Tel-e-phone to glo-ry Al-ways answers just in time.
God is on the throne—And you'll get the answer Thro' this royal tel-e-phone.
Mend the broken wire, Till your soul is burning With the Pen-te-cos-tal fire.
Dis-con-nect the line Held in constant keeping By the Father's hand divine.

D. S.—*We may talk to Je-sus Thro' this roy-al tel-e-phone.*

CHORUS.

Tel-e-phone to glo-ry, O what joy di-vine! I can feel the current

D. S.

Moving on the line; Built by God the Fa-ther For His loved and own—

He Cares For Even Me.

Avis B. Christiansen.

Harry Dixon Loes.

M. 72 = ♩   SOLO. *

1. My Heav'n-ly Fa - ther cares for e - ven me;...... His arms of
2. I can-not stray from out His pre-cious sight; .... Be-neath His
3. He cares for me— what peace un-told is mine! .... Tho' dark the

love sur-round me day by day;........ No night so dark that Je - sus
wings my soul doth rest se - cure; .... His hand of love will ev - er
way, He will not let me go;......... What-e'er be-fall, dear Lord, I

can - not see; .... He loves and cares for me al - way.
guide a - right;....... Kept by His pow'r I shall en - dure.
still am Thine,...... And Thou wilt care for me, I know.

CHORUS.

I know (I know) He cares for e - ven me; (for e-ven me;) He loves, (He loves,) He

cares so ten-der-ly; (so ten-der-ly;) I know (I know) not, Lord, how it can

He Cares For Even Me.

be, (how it can be,) But, oh, He cares (He cares) for e - ven me. (for e - ven me.)

99 The Hem of His Garment.

G. F. R.

COPYRIGHT, 1906. BY THE JOHN CHURCH CO.

Geo. F. Root.

1. She on - ly touch'd the hem of His gar - ment As to His side she stole,
2. She came in fear and trem-bling be - fore Him, She knew Her Lord had come;
3. He turn'd with "daughter be of good comfort, Thy faith hath made thee whole,"

A - mid the crowd that gathered a-round Him, And straightway she was whole.
She felt that from Him vir - tue had healed her, The might-y deed was done.
And peace that passeth all un - der-stand-ing With glad-ness filled her soul.

CHORUS.

Oh, touch the hem of His gar - ment And thou, too, shall be free;

His sav - ing pow'r this ve - ry hour Shall give new life to thee.

Take Up Thy Cross.

A. H. A.

Rev. A. H. Ackley.

Slowly with expression. M. 88 = ♩

1. I walked one day a-long a coun-try road, And there a stranger journeyed, too,
2. I cried, "Lord Jesus," and He spoke my name; I saw His hands all bruised and torn;
3. "O let me bear Thy cross, dear Lord," I cried, And, lo, a cross for me appeared,
4. My cross I'll car-ry till the crown ap-pears, The way I jour-ney soon will end

Bent low be-neath the burden of His load: It was a cross, a cross I knew.
I stooped to kiss a-way the marks of shame, The shame for me that He had borne.
The one for-got-ten, I had cast a-side, The one, so long, that I had feared.
Where God Himself shall wipe away all tears, And friend hold fellowship with friend.

CHORUS.

"Take up thy cross and follow Me," I hear the blessed Sav-ior call;

How can I make a less-er sac-ri-fice, When Je-sus gave His all?

101 Every Prayer Will Find Its Answer.

Mrs. Frank A. Breck.　　　　　　　　　　　Chas. H. Gabriel.

1. Ev - 'ry pray'r will find its an-swer— Ev - 'ry earn-est, trust-ing
2. He has prom-ised, "What-so - ev - er Ye shall ask, ye shall re-
3. Ev - 'ry pray'r will find its an-swer, Tho' it be in dis - tant
4. Ev - 'ry pray'r will find its an-swer, Let us cling with hope sub-

plea; Pray, and know that God is faith - ful, Tho' the
ceive;" Naught shall fail of blest ful - fill - ment, If we
years; Past our earth-ly time of test - ing, Past our
lime; To the prom - ise ev - er - last - ing, Reach - ing

CHORUS.

world un-faith - ful be! Ev - 'ry pray'r will find its
stead-fast-ly be - lieve. Ev - 'ry pray'r will find its
plead - ing and our tears.
past the bounds of time.

an - swer, For the word.......... of God is sure; Suns may
an - swer, For the word of God is sure;

fade .... and worlds may vanish, But His prom - ise shall en-dure.
Suns may fade But His prom-ise shall en-dure.

102 No Disappointment in Heaven.

F. M. L.

F. M. Lehman.
Har. by Miss Claudia Lehman.

M. 56 = ♩.

1. There's no dis-ap-point-ment in heaven,   No wear-i-ness, sor-row or pain;
2. We'll nev-er pay rent for our mansion,   The tax-es will nev-er come due;
3. There'll nev-er be crepe on the door-knob, No fu-ner-al train in the sky;

No hearts that are bleeding and bro-ken,   No song with a mi-nor re-frain;
Our garments will nev-er grow threadbare, But al-ways be fade-less and new;
No graves on the hill-sides of glo-ry,   For there we shall nev-er-more die;

The clouds of our earth-ly ho-ri-zon   Will nev-er ap-pear in the sky,
We'll nev-er be hun-gry nor thirst-y,   Nor lan-guish in pov-er-ty there,
The old will be young there for-ev-er,   Transformed in a mo-ment of time;

For all   will be sun-shine and gladness, With nev-er a sob nor a sigh.
For all   the rich bounties of heav-en   His sanc-ti-fied chil-dren will share.
Im-mor-tal we'll stand in His like-ness, The stars and the sun to out-shine.

CHORUS.

I'm bound for that beau-ti-ful cit-y   My Lord has prepared for His own;

No Disappointment in Heaven.

Where all the redeemed of all a-ges Sing "glo-ry" around the white throne;

Some-times I grow homesick for heaven, And the glo-ries I there shall be-hold:

rit.

What a joy that will be when my Sav-ior I see, In that beautiful cit-y of gold!

103 A Child of the King.

HATTIE E. BUELL.   REV. JOHN B. SUMNER, arr.

1. My Father is rich in houses and lands, He holdeth the wealth of the world in His hands!
2. My Father's own Son, the Saviour of men, Once wander'd on earth as the poorest of them.
3. I once was an outcast stranger on earth, A sinner by choice, and an alien by birth;
4. A tent or a cottage, why should I care? They're building a palace for me over there:

Of ru-bies and diamonds, of silver and gold, His coffers are full, He has riches un-told.
But now He is pleading our pardon on high, That we may be His when He comes by and by.
But I've been adopted, my name's written down, An heir to a mansion, a robe, and a crown.
Tho' exiled from home, yet, still I may sing: All glo-ry to God, I'm a child of the King.

CHORUS.

I'm a child of the King, A child of the King: With Jesus my Saviour I'm a child of the King.

That Was My Lord.

Arr. by C. H. G.

1. While passing a gar - den, I lingered to hear A voice faint and
2. So   deep were His sor - rows, so fer-vent His pray'rs, That down o'er His
3. "I   am thy Re-deem - er, for thee I must die, This cup is most
4. I   trembled with ter - ror, and loud-ly did cry: "Lord, save a poor

falt'ring, from one that was there; While pleading in anguish, the poor sin-ner's
bosom rolled sweat, blood and tears; I wept to be-hold Him, I asked Him His
bit - ter, but can-not pass by; Thy sins, like a mountain, are laid up - on
sin - ner! Oh! save, or I   die!" He cast His eyes on me, and said to me,

part,   The voice of the mourner af - fect-ed my heart. That was my
name; He answered, "Tis JESUS, from heaven I came." That was my
me,   And all this deep an-guish I   suf-fer for thee." That was my
"Live! Thy sins, which are man - y, I   free-ly for - give." That was my

Lord,   that was my Lord, That was my Lord who has suffered for me.
Lord,   that was my Lord, That was my Lord who has suffered for me.
Lord,   that was my Lord, That was my Lord who has suffered for me.
Lord,   that was my Lord, That was my Lord who has suffered for me.

105 No Night There.

JOHN R. CLEMENTS.   H. P. DANKS.

1. In the land of fade-less day Lies "the cit - y four-square,"
2. All the gates of pearl are made In "the cit - y four-square,"
3. And the gates shall nev - er close To "the cit - y four-square,"
4. There they need no sun-shine bright, In "that cit - y four-square."

It shall nev - er pass a - way, And there is "no night there."
All the streets with gold are laid, And there is "no night there."
There life's crys - tal riv - er flows, And there is "no night there."
For the Lamb is all the light, And there is "no night there."

CHORUS. mf

God shall "wipe a - way all tears;" There's no death, no pain, nor fears;
God shall "wipe a - way all tears;" There's no death, no pain, nor fears;

And they count not time by years, For there is no night there."
And they count not time by years, by years, For there is "no night . . . there."

106 The Great Judgment Morning.

Rev. Bert Shadduck.

L. L. Pickett.

M. 60 = ♩.

1. I dreamed that the great judgment morning Had dawned, and the trumpet had blown;
2. The rich man was there, but his mon - ey Had melt - ed and van-ished a - way;
3. The wid - ow was there with the or-phans, God heard and remembered their cries;
4. The mor - al man came to the judgment, But his self-righteous rags would not do;

I dreamed that the na-tions had gath-ered To judg-ment be-fore the white throne;
A pau - per he stood in the judg-ment, His debts were too heav-y to pay;
No sor - row in heav-en for - ev - er, God wiped all the tears from their eyes;
The men who had cru-ci-fied Je - sus Had passed off as mor - al men, too;

From the throne came a bright shin-ing an-gel And stood on the land and the sea,
The great man was there, but his great-ness, When death came, was left far be-hind!
The gambler was there and the drunkard, And the man that had sold them the drink,
The soul that had put off sal-va-tion—"Not to-night; I'll get saved by-and-by;

And swore with his hand raised to heav-en, That time was no lon-ger to be.
The an - gel that o-pened the rec-ords, Not a trace of his greatness could find.
With the peo-ple who gave him the license—To - geth - er in hell they did sink.
No time now to think of re - li-gion!" At last they had found time to die.

The Great Judgment Morning.

CHORUS.

And oh, what a weeping and wail-ing, As the lost were told of their fate;

rit.

They cried for the rocks and the mountains, They prayed, but their prayer was too late.

107 An Evening Prayer.

C. M. Battersby.
Arr. by C. H. G.

Chas. H. Gabriel.

1. If I have wounded an-y soul to-day, It I have caused one foot to
2. If I have ut-tered i-dle words or vain, If I have turned a-side from
3. If I have been perverse or hard, or cold, If I have longed for shel-ter
4. Forgive the sins I have confessed to Thee; Forgive the se-cret sins I

go a-stray, If I have walked in my own wil-ful way, Dear Lord, for-give!
want or pain, Lest I myself shall suffer thro' the strain, Dear Lord, for-give!
in Thy fold, When Thou hast given me some fort to hold, Dear Lord, for-give!
do not see; O guide me, love me, and my Keep-er be, A-men.

108 Life's Railway to Heaven.

(Respectfully dedicated to the railroad men).

M. E. Abbey.

Charlie D. Tillman.

Solo or Duet. *Tempo ad lib.*

M. 72 = ♩

1. Life is like a moun-tain rail-road, With an en-gi-neer that's brave;
2. You will roll up grades of tri-al; You will cross the bridge of strife;
3. You will oft-en find ob-struc-tions; Look for storms of wind and rain;
4. As you roll a-cross the tres-tle, Spanning Jor-dan's swell-ing tide,

We must make the run suc-cess-ful, From the cra-dle to the grave;
See that Christ is your con-duc-tor On this light-ning train of life;
On a fill, or curve, or tres-tle, They will al-most ditch your train;
You be-hold the Un-ion De-pot In-to which your train will glide;

Watch the curves, the fills, the tun-nels; Nev-er fal-ter, nev-er quail;
Al-ways mind-ful of ob-struc-tion, Do your du-ty, nev-er fail;
Put your trust a-lone in Je-sus; Nev-er fal-ter, nev-er fail;
There you'll meet the Su-perin-ten-dent, God the Fa-ther, God the Son,

rit.

Keep your hand up-on the throt-tle, And your eye up-on the rail.
Keep your hand up-on the throt-tle, And your eye up-on the rail.
Keep your hand up-on the throt-tle, And your eye up-on the rail.
With the heart-y, joy-ous plaud-it, "Wea-ry pil-grim, wel-come home!"

CHORUS.

Bless-ed Sav-ior, Thou wilt guide us Till we reach that bliss-ful shore;

Life's Railway to Heaven.

Where the an - gels wait to join us In Thy praise for - ev - er - more.

109 Though Your Sins Be As Scarlet.

FANNY J. CROSBY. (Isaiah 1 : 18.) WILLIAM H. DOANE.

DUET. *Gently.*

1. "Tho' your sins be as scar-let, They shall be as white as snow; as snow;
2. Hear the voice that entreats you; O re-turn ye un-to God! to God!
3. He'll forgive your transgressions, And remember them no more; no more;

QUARTET.

Tho' they be red......... like crim-son, They shall be as wool;"
He is of great......... com-pas-sion, And of won-drous love;
"Look un-to me,.......... ye peo-ple," Saith the Lord your God:

Tho' they be red

DUET. *p*   QUARTET.   *f*

"Tho' your sins be as scar-let, Tho' your sins be as scar-let,
Hear the voice that en-treats you, Hear the voice that en-treats you,
He'll for-give your trans-gres-sions, He'll for-give your transgressions,

p ritard.

They shall be as white as snow, They shall be as white as snow."
O re-turn ye un-to God! O re-turn ye un-to God!
And re-mem-ber them no more, And re-mem-ber them no more.

110 Laying My Treasure Up There.

Rev. Johnson Oatman, Jr.

Chas. H. Gabriel.

1. On the moun-tain of Zi-on be-yond the blue sky, Stands a
2. There's a man-sion a-wait-ing God's peo-ple, I'm told, Which the
3. All the love of my heart, and my soul, mind and strength, And the
4. So al-tho' a poor pil-grim on earth I may roam, Ev-er

cit-y so won-drous and fair; I ex-pect to de-part for that
Sav-ior has gone to pre-pare; There the walls are of jas-per, the
work that with Je-sus I share, Are but some of the rich-es I'll
con-stant in watch-ing and prayer, Soon I'll hear the glad summons to

CHORUS.

land, by and by,—For I'm lay-ing my treas-ure up there.
streets are of gold, I am lay-ing my treas-ure up there. I am lay-ing my
find there at length,—For I'm lay-ing my treas-ure up there.
start for my home, For I'm lay-ing my treas-ure up there.

slow.

treasure up there, up there, In that beau-ti-ful cit-y so fair;.... When its
so fair;

glories un-fold I'll have rich-es un-told, For I'm lay-ing my treasure up there.

111 My Mother's Prayer.

J. W. Van De Venter.   W. S. Weeden.

M. 66 = ♩

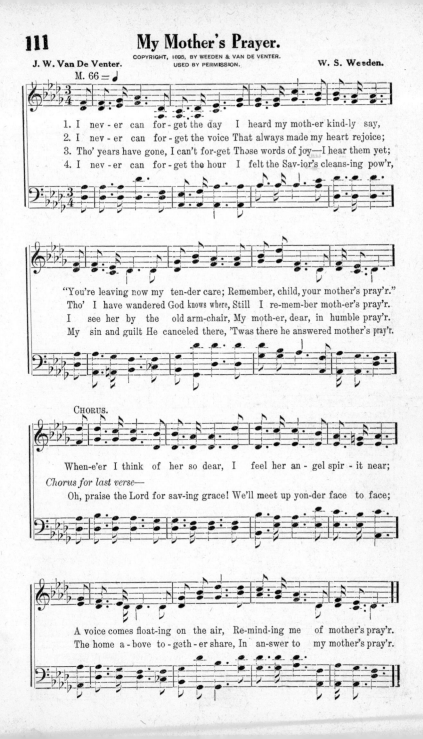

1. I nev-er can for-get the day I heard my moth-er kind-ly say,
2. I nev-er can for-get the voice That always made my heart rejoice;
3. Tho' years have gone, I can't for-get Those words of joy—I hear them yet;
4. I nev-er can for-get the hour I felt the Sav-ior's cleans-ing pow'r,

"You're leaving now my ten-der care; Remember, child, your mother's pray'r."
Tho' I have wandered God knows where, Still I re-mem-ber moth-er's pray'r.
I see her by the old arm-chair, My moth-er, dear, in humble pray'r.
My sin and guilt He canceled there, 'Twas there he answered mother's pray'r.

CHORUS.

When-e'er I think of her so dear, I feel her an-gel spir-it near;
Chorus for last verse—
Oh, praise the Lord for sav-ing grace! We'll meet up yon-der face to face;

A voice comes float-ing on the air, Re-mind-ing me of mother's pray'r.
The home a-bove to-geth-er share, In an-swer to my mother's pray'r.

112 More Like Him.

Rev. W. C. Poole.

B. D. Ackley.

DUET. M. 88

1. There's a prayer I am pray-ing to-day,   And it dai-ly grows
2. There's a mar-vel-ous dream that I dream   Of a won-der-ful
3. There's a song I am sing-ing to-day,   'Tis a song that is

dear-er to me,   As I look to my Sav-ior and pray—   That I
Sav-ior di-vine;   And I wak-en to pray that my dream   May be
breathing my prayer,   As my Sav-ior is lead-ing my way—   That all

al-ways more like Him may be.............
real, and His like-ness be mine............ More like the Mas-ter in
oth-ers His like-ness may share...........

thought and deed,   More like the Mas-ter, for this I plead; Close by His

side as He walks with me,   More like the Mas-ter I would be.

113 Christ Died.

F. A.

Frances Abernethy.

1. I do not un - der-stand how it can be...... That e - ven
2. So wast-ed and so lost my life has been,... I have no
3. And O, so might - y was the sac - ri - fice,.... So great th'a-

Thou canst heal a soul like me; But this I know, and in that
power to cleanse my-self from sin; And so to Thee, for - get - ting
tone - ment made for all our lives, That this I know,— I shall not

CHORUS.

sure - ty hide,—I on - ly know Christ died.
all my pride, I humbly plead—Christ died. O Lord, I come; I have no
be de - nied, Since 'twas for me Christ died.

worth to plead, I have no of - f'ring but my sin - ful need; But O, to

Thee who hath the way sup - plied, I on - ly say—Christ died!

114 Who Could It Be?

Fred P. Morris.

Robert Harkness.

DUET. M. 80 =

1. Some-bod-y came and lift-ed me Out of my sin and mis-er-
2. Some-bod-y bent so ten-der-ly, Pleading so long and pa-tient-
3. Some-bod-y whis-pered sweet and low, Tell-ing me just the way to
4. Some-bod-y holds my hand each day, Guid-ing my feet lest I should

y, Some-bod-y came, oh, who could it be, Who could it
ly, Some-bod-y came, oh, who could it be, Who could it
go, Some-bod-y spoke, I lis-tened, and lo, Who could it
stray, Walk-ing with Him how bless-ed the way, Who could it

CHORUS.

be but Je - sus? Who could it be, O who could it
Je - - sus, Je -

be? Who could it be but Je - sus? Who could it
sus, Je - -

be, O who could it be? Who could it be but Je - sus?
sus, yes, Je - - sus,

rall.

pp

115 Into the Woods My Master Went.

Sidney Lanier.   **J. B. Herbert.**

Andante. M. 60 = ♩.

1. In - to the woods my Mas - ter went, Clean for - spent, for - spent:
2. Out of the woods my Mas - ter went, And He was well con - tent:

In - to the woods my Mas - ter came, For - spent with love and shame.
Out of the woods my Mas - ter came, Con - tent with death and shame.

But the ol - ives were not blind to Him; The lit - tle gray leaves were
When death and shame would woo Him last, From un - der the trees they

kind to Him; The thorn - tree had a mind to Him, When
drew Him last; 'Twas on a tree they slew Him last, When

in - to the woods He came, When in - to the woods He came.
out of the woods He came, When out of the woods He came.

116 My Savior.

Words and music by CHAS. M. FILLMORE.

May be sung as a Solo or Duet.

1. I've a Sav - iour, kind and tender, I've a Sav - iour full of grace,
2. For my sake He came from heaven To this world of sin and shame;
3. Tho' I've oft - en been un-worth-y, He has con-stant been, and true;
4. I've a Sav - iour, kind and tender, He would be your Saviour, too;

And a smile of winning sweetness, Ev - er beams up - on His face.
Bore my guilt, tho' He was guiltless, And tho' blame-less, took my blame.
Tho' I wronged Him, He forgave me When I would my vows re-new;
Will you not ac-cept the par-don Which He free - ly of-fers you?

In my heart's shrine of af-fec - tion, He shall hold the highest place.
Can I ev - er cease to love Him, And His good-ness to proclaim?
Tho' I spurned Him, He with kindness My re - bel-lious heart would woo.
Take Him now as your Re-deem-er, Earth has not a friend so true.

CHORUS.

How I love Him, How I love Him; Since for
How I love Him, How I love Him,

me,........ He bled and died, How I love....... Him
Since for me He bled and died, How I love Him,

My Saviour.

Yes, I love Him   more than all.......... the world be-side.
Yes, I love Him,   more than all

---

117   ## Even the Waifs of the Street.

J. A. Fraser, Jr.   Fred Weldon, Arr.

M. 56 = ♩.

1. Je - sus loves chil-dren, the bi - ble says so; He will be with them where
2. "Suf-fer the chil-dren, to come un - to me," These words He spoke be - side
3. Rag-ged, and tat-tered, and hun-gry, the waif May to the Sav - ior re -

ev - er they go,   Shield them from harm thro' the dark-ness of night,
blue Gal - i - lee;   Not the rich on - ly His sweet mes-sage greets,
pair and be safe;   He once was hun-gry and friend-less, and poor,

CHORUS.

Guide them and help them all day to do right.
Je - sus loves e - ven the waifs of the street. Shout the glad news to
That's why He pit - ies the waifs at the door.

each one you meet; Je - sus loves e - ven the waifs of the street!

118 Shadows.

C. H. G.

COPYRIGHT, 1920, BY HOMER A. RODEHEAVER.
INTERNATIONAL COPYRIGHT SECURED.

Chas. H. Gabriel.

M. 108 = ♪

1. When the sun of life fades in-to crim-son and gold, And the
2. I shall stand on the shore of the Mys-ter-y Sea, Shrink-ing
3. As the length-en-ing shad-ows are lost in the gloom, And I

mists of e-ter-ni-ty o'er me have rolled, I shall
not at the dark-ness, though deep it may be; "For I
walk thro' the mid-night with Death, in the tomb, A new

look thro' the shadows that fall with the night, And catch the bright gleam of the
know in whom I have be-liev-ed," and fear No shad-ow or dan-ger, for
Star will a-rise o'er the night of the grave, And Je-sus will come in His

Cit-y of Light.
He will be near.
pow-er to save.

Chorus.

Shad-ows? Yes, shad-ows I know will be there!

Shad-ows? Yes shad-ows! but not of de-spair! For morn-ing will break,

Shadows.

And I shall a-wake To dwell with my King, and His glo-ry share.

119 ## Till the Last Bugle Blows.

Charlotte G. Homer.

COPYRIGHT, 1919, BY HOMER A. RODEHEAVER.

Chas. H. Gabriel.

M. 112 = ♩

1. Wrapped in the col-ors he died in de-fend-ing, We pay our last
2. Faith-ful and loy-al, pri-va-tion dis-dain-ing, His bos-om he
3. Sleep-ing he lies 'neath a ha-lo of glo-ry, And o-ver his

trib-ute a-bove his re-pose; Brave-ly he stood, for our
bared to the steel of our foes; Fight-ing—a he-ro till
bed we will plant the wild rose; Fear-less, un-daunt-ed on

hon-or con-tend-ing, But now let him rest till the last bu-gle blows,
death un-com-plain-ing, But now let him rest till the last bu-gle blows,
bat-tle-fields go-ry, But now let him rest till the last bu-gle blows,

BUGLE. *pp*

Now let him rest till the last bu-gle blows.
Now let him rest till the last bu-gle blows.
Now let him rest till the last bu-gle blows.

120 Jesus Thinks of Me.

James Rowe.
DUET.

B. D. Ackley.

1. This I know, when storms are sweeping, This I know, when worn by reap-ing,
2. When sweet com-fort I would borrow, Strength and cour - age for the mor-row,
3. This I know, when foes as - sail me, Or when e - vil pleasures hail me,
4. When my soul shall reach the riv - er And from loved ones I must sev - er,

I am in my Sav-ior's keep-ing, And He thinks of me.
Read-y to re - lieve my sor - row, Je - sus thinks of me.
Grace di - vine will nev - er fail me, Je - sus thinks of me.
This will be my com-fort ev - er, Je - sus thinks of me.

CHORUS.

Je-sus thinks of me, yes, He thinks of me, Je-sus thinks of me and waits to bless;

This will be my com-fort ev - er-more, Je - sus thinks of me.

121 When You Know Jesus Too.

Ina Duley Ogdon.

B. D. Ackley.

Melody in 2nd Tenor.

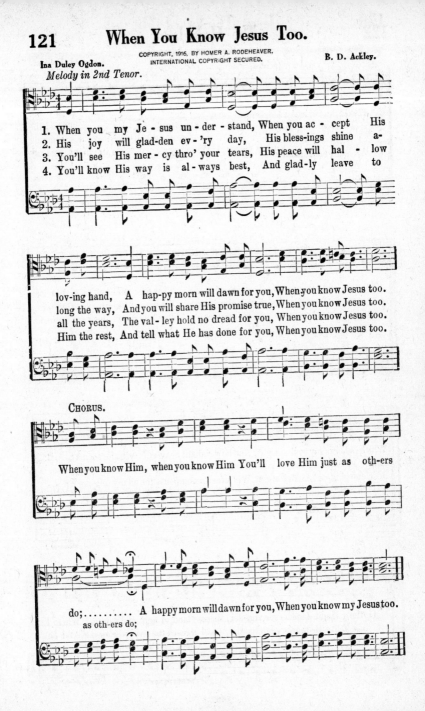

1. When you my Je-sus un-der-stand, When you ac-cept His
2. His joy will glad-den ev-'ry day, His bless-ings shine a-
3. You'll see His mer-cy thro' your tears, His peace will hal-low
4. You'll know His way is al-ways best, And glad-ly leave to

lov-ing hand, A hap-py morn will dawn for you, When you know Jesus too.
long the way, And you will share His promise true, When you know Jesus too.
all the years, The val-ley hold no dread for you, When you know Jesus too.
Him the rest, And tell what He has done for you, When you know Jesus too.

CHORUS.

When you know Him, when you know Him You'll love Him just as oth-ers
do;......... A happy morn will dawn for you, When you know my Jesus too.
as oth-ers do;

The Homeland.

C. H. G.

Chas. H. Gabriel.

M. 84 =

1. When the beau-ties of the Homeland Burst up - on my rav-ished sight, And the
2. Gold-en streets thro-'out the cit - y, Pearl-y gates and jas - per walls, Shin-ing
3. When the sil - ver cord is loosened, When my spir - it takes its flight, And my

King in all His beau-ty I shall see,...... Then how small will seem the trials
throngs who sweetly chant their Maker's praise; Where no sickness ev - er en-ters,
soul shall from this cumb'rous clay be free,.... Just one note of heav-en's mu-sic,

Which did here my soul affright, And how radiant heav-en's splendor seems to me!
And no shad-ow ev - er falls, Naught to mar the joy of ev - er-last - ing praise.
Just one glimpse of glory bright, Will sweet recompense for all my toil-ing be.

CHORUS.

O the { Home-land o - ver yon-der, Blessed land of light and won-der, Where I
{ lit - tle more rough tossing, And I'll reach the river's cross-ing, And be

The Homeland.

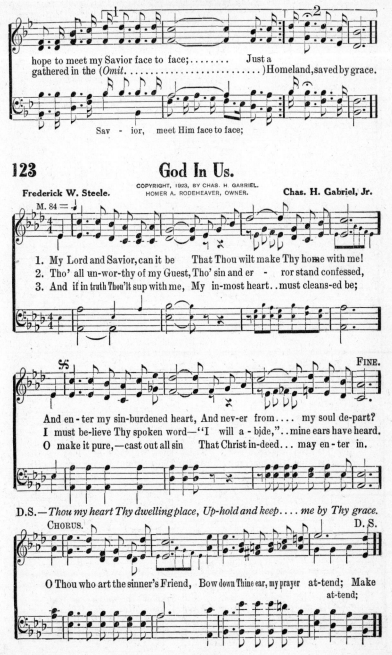

hope to meet my Savior face to face;........ Just a
gathered in the (*Omit*..........................)Homeland, saved by grace.

Sav - ior, meet Him face to face;

123

God In Us.

COPYRIGHT, 1923, BY CHAS. H. GABRIEL.
HOMER A. RODEHEAVER, OWNER.

Frederick W. Steele.   Chas. H. Gabriel, Jr.

M. 84 = ♩

1. My Lord and Savior, can it be   That Thou wilt make Thy home with me!
2. Tho' all un-wor-thy of my Guest, Tho' sin and er - ror stand confessed,
3. And if in truth Thou'lt sup with me, My in-most heart..must cleans-ed be;

FINE.

And en - ter my sin-burdened heart, And nev-er from.... my soul de-part?
I must be-lieve Thy spoken word—"I will a - bide,".. mine ears have heard.
O make it pure,—cast out all sin   That Christ in-deed... may en - ter in.

D.S.—*Thou my heart Thy dwelling place, Up-hold and keep.... me by Thy grace.*

CHORUS.   D.S.

O Thou who art the sinner's Friend, Bow down Thine ear, my prayer at-tend; Make
at-tend;

124 His Eye is On the Sparrow.

Mrs. C. D. Martin. **Chas. H. Gabriel.**

M. 56 = .

1. Why should I feel dis-cour-aged, Why should the shad-ows come,
2. "Let not your heart be trou-bled," His ten-der word I hear,
3. When-ev - er I am tempt-ed, When-ev - er clouds a - rise,

Why should my heart be lone-ly,.... And long for heav'n and home, When
And rest-ing on His good-ness,.. I lose my doubts and fears; Tho'
When song gives place to sigh-ing,... When hope with-in me dies, I

Je - sus is my por - tion? My con-stant friend is He: His
by the path He lead - eth, But one step I may see: His
draw the clos - er to Him, From care He sets me free; His

eye is on the spar-row, And I know He watch-es me; His
eye is on the spar-row, And I know He watch-es me; His
eye is on the spar-row, And I know He cares for me; His

eye is on the spar - row, And I know He watch-es me.
eye is on the spar - row, And I know He watch-es me.
eye is on the spar - row, And I know He cares for me

His Eye is On the Sparrow.

CHORUS.

I sing be-cause I'm happy, ... I sing because I'm free, . . .
I'm hap-py,
I'm free,

rall.

For His eye is on the spar-row, And I know He watches me.

---

125 Fill Me Now.

E. H. Stokes.

COPYRIGHT, 1905, BY MRS. L. E. SWENEY. RENEWAL.

Jno. R. Sweney.

M. 120

1. Hov - er o'er me, Ho - ly Spir - it, Bathe my trem-bling heart and brow;
2. Thou canst fill me, gra-cious Spir - it, Though I can - not tell Thee how;
3. I am weak-ness, full of weak-ness, At Thy sa - cred feet I bow;
4. Cleanse and comfort, bless and save me, Bathe, O bathe my heart and brow;

FINE.

Fill me with Thy hal-lowed pres-ence, Come, O come, and fill me now.
But I need Thee, great-ly need Thee, Come, O come, and fill me now.
Blest, di - vine, e - ter - nal Spir - it, Fill with pow'r, and fill me now.
Thou art com-fort - ing and sav - ing, Thou art sweet - ly fill - ing now.

D.S.–*Fill me with Thy hal-lowed pres-ence, Come, O come and fill me now.*

D. S.

Fill me now, fill me now, Je - sus, come, and fill me now;

126 Have You Counted the Cost?

A. J. H.

A. J. Hodge.

1. There's a line that is drawn by re-ject-ing our Lord, Where the call of His
2. You may bar - ter your hope of e - ter - ri-ty's morn, For a mo-ment of
3. While the door of His mer - cy is o - pen to you, Ere the depth of His

Spir - it is lost,.... And you hur - ry a - long with the pleasure-mad throng—
joy at the most,... For the glit - ter of sin and the things it will win—
love you ex - haust, .. Won't you come and be healed, won't you whisper, I yield—

rit. *p* **CHORUS.** *rit.*

Have you counted, have you counted the cost?
Have you counted, have you counted the cost? Have you counted the cost, if your
I have counted, I have counted the cost?

pp *a tempo.*

soul should be lost, Tho' you gain the whole world for your own?.... E - ven

rit. *p*

now it may be that the line you have crossed, Have you counted, have you counted the cost?

127
They Led Him Away.

Herbert Buffum
and C. H. G.

Chas. H. Gabriel.

M. 116 = ♩

1 They led Him a-way to be cru-ci-fied, The meek and low-ly
2. They led Him a-way—nor did He re-bel, The great, re-deem-ing
3. They led Him a-way—and He died for me, The lov-ing, liv-ing

Je-sus! And there on the cross, between thieves He died, My won-der-ful,
Je-sus! The an-guish He suf-fered no tongue can tell This won-der-ful,
Je-sus! I'll fol-low His steps till His face I see, This won-der-ful,

Chorus.

won-der-ful Je-sus. They led Him a-way, they led Him a-way

To Cal-va-ry's rug-ged cross!...... He fol-lowed, a-lone,

dim. *ad lib.*

Our sins to a-tone, This won-der-ful, won-der-ful Je-sus.

128

What Then?

Elisha A. Hoffman.   W. S. Nickle

M. 138 = ♪

1. Aft - er the pleas-ures of life are o'er, And you shall stand, face
2. Aft - er the puls-es shall cease to beat, When at the throne of
3. Aft - er your heart   is hushed and still, Aft - er the death-dews,
4. Aft - er the trum - pet's aw - ful blast, Aft - er the judg-ment

to   the shore Of the dim land of the   ev - er-more, Care - less
Lord you meet, Wait-ing your doom at the judg-ment seat, Care - less
damp and chill, O - ver your frame of mor - tal - i-ty thrill, Care - less
shall be past, When you have come to your doom at last, Poor, lost

soul, what then? Care-less soul, what then? Care - less soul, what then?
soul, what then? Care-less soul, what then? Care - less soul, what then?
soul, what then? Care-less soul, what then? Care - less soul, what then?
soul, what then? Poor, lost soul, what then? Poor, lost soul, what then?

Aft - er the pleas-ures of life are o'er, Care - less soul, what then?
Wait-ing your doom at the judg-ment seat, Care - less soul, what then?
Aft - er your heart   is hushed and still, Care - less soul, what then?
When you have come to your doom at last, Poor, lost soul, what then?

129
That's Why I Love Him.

S. L. Arr.

Scott Lawrence.

M. 138

1. Je - sus has prom - ised my Shep - herd to be, That's why I
2. He the weak lambs to His bos - om will take, That's why I
3. He has in heav - en pre - pared me a place, That's why I

love Him so;.... And to the chil - dren He said, "Come to Me,"
love Him so;.... Nev - er will He for a mo - ment for - sake,
love Him so;.... Where I may dwell, by His won - der - ful grace,

CHORUS.

That's why I love Him so..... That's why I love Him, That's why I
love Him, Be - cause He first loved me;....... When I'm tempt - ed and
loved me;

tried, He is close by my side,... That's why I love Him so....

130 Only the Childlike.

Jesse P. Tompkins.

B. D. Ackley.

M. 100 = ♩

1. On - ly the child - like find the way In - to the
2. On - ly the child - like find the door In - to the
3. On - ly the child - like rest se - cure, Hold - ing the

realm of per - fect day; No oth - er wis - dom
fold when tem - pests roar, Where safe - ly rest the
an - chor safe and sure, When on the wa - ters

'neath the skies, Ev - er will o - pen our blind - ed eyes.
shel - tered sheep, Tho' i - cy blasts o'er the moun - tains sweep.
dark and deep, Trust - ing the Hand that will ev - er keep.

CHORUS.

Sweet - ly trust, sim - ply trust, Light will come to thee;

Tho' by earth - ly shad - ows blind - ed, Thou shalt sure - ly see.

131 My Mother's Bible.

M. B. Williams.   COPYRIGHT, 1921, BY CHARLIE D. TILLMAN. RENEWAL.   Charlie D. Tillman.

1. There's a dear and precious Book, Tho' it's worn and fad-ed now, Which re-
2. As she read the sto-ries o'er Of those mighty men of old, Of
3. Then she read of Je-sus' love, As He blest the chil-dren dear, How He
4. Well, those days are past and gone, But their mem'ry lin-gers still, And the

calls those hap-py days of long a-go, When I stood at mother's knee,
Jo-seph and of Dan-iel and their trials, Of lit-tle Da-vid bold,
suf-fered, bled and died up-on the tree; Of His heav-y load of care,
dear old Book each day has been my guide; And I seek to do His will,

FINE.

With her hand up-on my brow, And I heard her voice in gen-tle tones and low.
Who be-came a king at last, Of Sa-tan and his man-y wick-ed wiles.
Then she dried my flow-ing tears With her kisses as she said it was for me.
As my moth-er taught me then, And ev-er in my heart His words abide.

D. S.–As I walk the nar-row way That leads at last to that bright home above.

CHORUS.

Bless-ed Book,...... pre-cious Book,...... On thy dear old tear-stained
Bless-ed Book,   precious Book,

D. S.

leaves I love to look;......... Thou art sweet-er day by day,
love to look;

132 The Handwriting on the Wall.

K. Shaw.   Knowles Shaw

1. At the feast of Bel - shaz-zar and a thous-and of his lords,
2. See the brave cap - tive Dan - iel as he stood be - fore the throng,
3. See the faith, zeal, and cour-age, that would dare to do the right,
4. So our deeds are re - cord - ed, there's a Hand that's writ-ing now,

While they drank from gold-en ves-sels, as the book of truth re - cords;
And re-buked the haughty mon-arch for his might - y deeds of wrong;
Which the spir - it gave to Dan - iel, this the se - cret of his might;
Sin - ner, give your heart to Je - sus, to His roy - al man-date bow;

In the night as they rev - el'd In the roy - al pal - ace hall,
As he read out the writ-ing, 'twas the doom of one and all,
In his home in Ju - de - a, or a cap - tive in the hall,
For the day is ap-proach-ing, it must come to one and all,

They were seized with con-ster - na - tion at the hand up - on the wall.
For the king-dom now was finished—said the hand up - on the wall.
He un - der-stood the writ-ing of his God up - on the wall.
When the sin - ner's con-dem - na - tion, will be writ - ten on the wall.

CHORUS.

'Tis the hand of God · on the wall,   'Tis the hand of God

The Handwriting on the Wall.

on the wall; ...... Shall the re-cord be "Found wanting," or shall

it be "Found trusting?," While that hand is writ-ing on the wall ......

133. I Surrender All.

Copyright, 1896, by Weeden & Van De Venter. P. P. Billhorn, owner.

J. W. Van De Venter.   W. S. Weeden.

M. 92 = ♩

1. { All to Je-sus I sur-ren-der, All to Him I free-ly give; / I will ev-er love and trust Him, In His presence dai-ly live. }

2. { All to Je-sus I sur-ren-der, Hum-bly at His feet I bow; / World-ly pleasures all for-sak-en, Take me, Je-sus, take me now. }

3. { All to Je-sus I sur-ren-der, Make me, Sav-ior, whol-ly Thine; / Let me feel the Ho-ly Spir-it, Tru-ly know that Thou art mine. }

4. { All to Je-sus I sur-ren-der Now I feel the sa-cred flame; / O the joy of full sal-va-tion! Glo-ry, glo-ry to His name! }

CHORUS.

I sur-ren-der all, I sur-ren-der all;
I sur-ren-der all, I sur-ren-der all;

All to Thee, my bless-ed Sav-ior, I sur-ren-der all.

Unanswered Yet.

Charlie D. Tillman.

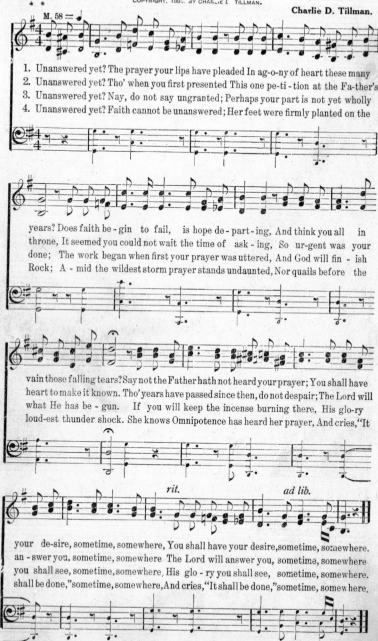

1. Unanswered yet? The prayer your lips have pleaded In ag-o-ny of heart these many
2. Unanswered yet? Tho' when you first presented This one pe-ti-tion at the Fa-ther's
3. Unanswered yet? Nay, do not say ungranted; Perhaps your part is not yet wholly
4. Unanswered yet? Faith cannot be unanswered; Her feet were firmly planted on the

years? Does faith be-gin to fail, is hope de-part-ing, And think you all in
throne, It seemed you could not wait the time of ask-ing, So ur-gent was your
done; The work began when first your prayer was uttered, And God will fin-ish
Rock; A-mid the wildest storm prayer stands undaunted, Nor quails before the

vain those falling tears? Say not the Father hath not heard your prayer; You shall have
heart to make it known. Tho' years have passed since then, do not despair; The Lord will
what He has be-gun. If you will keep the incense burning there, His glo-ry
loud-est thunder shock. She knows Omnipotence has heard her prayer, And cries, "It

rit. *ad lib.*

your de-sire, sometime, somewhere, You shall have your desire, sometime, somewhere.
an-swer you, sometime, somewhere The Lord will answer you, sometime, somewhere
you shall see, sometime, somewhere, His glo-ry you shall see, sometime, somewhere.
shall be done," sometime, somewhere, And cries, "It shall be done," sometime, somewhere.

135 Grace Greater Than Our Sin.

Julia H. Johnston.

D. B. Towner.

M. 144

1. Mar - vel - ous grace of our lov - ing Lord, Grace that ex - ceeds our
2. Sin and de - spair like the sea waves cold, Threat - en the soul with
3. Dark is the stain that we can - not hide, What can a - vail to
4. Mar - vel - ous, in - fi - nite, match - less grace, Free - ly be - stowed on

sin and our guilt, Yon - der on Cal - va - ry's mount out - poured,
in - fi - nite loss; Grace that is great - er, yes, grace un - told,
wash it a - way? Look! there is flow - ing a crim - son tide;
all who be - lieve; You that are long - ing to see His face,

CHORUS.

There where the blood of the Lamb was spilt.
Points to the Ref - uge, the Might - y Cross. Grace, grace,
Whit - er than snow you may be to - day. Mar - vel - ous grace,
Will you this mo - ment His grace re - ceive?

God's grace, Grace that will par - don and cleanse with - in; Grace,
In - fi - nite grace, Mar - vel - ous

grace, God's grace, Grace that is great - er than all our sin.
grace, In - fi - nite grace,

136 He Gave Himself For Me.

J. W. V.

J. W. Van DeVenter.

DUET.

M. 80

1. The debt I owed I could not pay, For I was help-less from the fall;
2. The way was dark, I could not see, My hope was gone, my faith was small,
3. By faith I saw Him bleed and die! That dreadful day I now re-call,
4. He saved my soul that once was lost, He res-cued me, a worth-less thrall;
5. I found a place with-in His care, The gates of death can-not ap-pall;

Yet still I heard the Spir-it say That Je - sus paid it all.
Un - til the Word re-vealed to me That Je - sus paid it all.
When noth-ing else could sat - is - fy, Then Je - sus paid it all.
I won-der, when I count the cost, Why Je - sus paid it all.
His grace will keep me ev - er there, For Je - sus paid it all.

CHORUS.

He paid my debt up - on the cross, He died to set me free;

When noth - ing else could pay the loss, He gave Him - self for me.

137 O Love That Will Not Let Me Go.

Rev. Geo. Matheson. COPYRIGHT, 1910, BY HOMER A. RODEHEAVER. J. B. Herbert.

May be sung as duet, Soprano and Tenor.

M. 76 =

1. O love that will not let me go, I rest my
2. O light that fol-lowest all my way I yield my
3. O joy that seek-est me thro' pain, I can - not
4. O cross that lift-est up my head, I dare not

wea - ry soul in Thee; I give Thee back the life I
flick-'ring torch to Thee; My heart re - stores its bor-rowed
close my heart to Thee; I trace the rain - bow thro' the
ask to fly from Thee; I lay in dust life's glo - ry

owe, That in Thine o - cean depths its flow May
ray, That in Thy sun-shine's blaze its day May
rain, And feel the prom - ise is not vain That
dead, And from the ground there blos - soms red Life

rich - er, full - er be, May rich - er, full - er be.
bright - er, fair - er be, May bright - er, fair - er be.
morn shall tear - less be, That morn shall tear - less be.
that shall end - less be, Life that shall end - less be.

The Ninety and Nine.

Elizabeth C. Clephane.

Ira D. Sankey.

1. There were nine-ty and nine that safe - ly lay   In the shel - ter of the
2. "Lord,   Thou   hast here Thy ninety and nine; Are they not e - nough for

fold,   But one was out on the hills a-way, Far off from the gates of
Thee?" But the Shepherd made an-swer: "'Tis of mine has wandered away from

gold; A - way on the mount-ains wild and bare, A - way from the
me; And al - though the road be rough and steep I go to the

ten - der Shep-herd's care, A - way from the ten - der Shepherd's care.
desert to find my sheep, I go to the desert to find my sheep."

3 But none of the ransomed ever knew
    How deep were the waters crossed;
Or how dark was the night that the Lord
    passed through
Ere He found His sheep that was lost.
Out in the desert He heard its cry—
Sick and helpless, and ready to die.

4 "Lord, whence are those blood-drops all
    the way
That mark out the mountain's track?"
They were shed for one who had gone
    astray

Ere the Shepherd could bring him back
"Lord whence are Thy hands so rent
    and torn?"
"They are pierced to-night by many a
    thorn."

5 But all thro' the mountains, thunder-riven,
    And up from the rocky steep,
There rose a cry to the gate of heaven,
    "Rejoice! I have found my sheep!"
And the angels echoed around the throne,
    "Rejoice, for the Lord bring back His
    own!"

139   When They Ring the Golden Bells.

Dion De Marbelle.

M. 80 = ♩

1. There's a land be-yond the riv-er, That we call the sweet for-ev-er, And we
2. We shall know no sin nor sor-row, In that ha-ven of to-mor-row, When our
3. When our days shall know their number, When in death we sweet-ly slumber, When the

on-ly reach that shore by faith's decree; One by one we'll gain the portals, There to
barque shall sail beyond the sil-ver sea; We shall on-ly know the blessing Of our
King commands the spir-it to be free; Nev-er-more with anguish la-den, We shall

FINE.

dwell with the immortals, When they ring the golden bells for you and me.
Father's sweet caressing, When they ring the golden bells for you and me.
reach that love-ly ai-den, When they ring the golden bells for you and me.

you and me.

D.S.–yond the shining river, When they ring the golden bells for you and me.

CHORUS.

Don't you hear the bells now ringing? Don't you hear the an-gels sing-ing? 'Tis the

D. S.

glo-ry hal-le-lu-jah Ju-bi-lee. (Ju-bi-lee.) In that far-off sweet forever, Just be-

140 Where They Never Say "Good-bye."

Rev. A. H. Ackley.

B. D. Ackley.

M. 92 = ♩ Solo.—*Do not hurry.*

1. There's a land where the birds are ev - er sing - ing, Where the flow'rs in their
2. We shall tell of the way that we have trav-eled, When at last we shall
3. We shall gaze on His face in ad - o - ra - tion, Joy re-splen-dent shall

beau-ty nev - er fade, Where the joy-bells of love are ev - er ring - ing,
en - ter heav-en's door, And the prob-lems of life will be un - rav - eled,
thrill our souls a - new, As we crown Him the King of our sal - va - tion,

Chorus.

And no e - vil shall ev - er dare in-vade.
When we meet on that bright e - ter - nal shore. In the land where they
And e - ter - ni-ty's glo-ries come to view.

nev - er say good-bye, No sad part-ings, for none shall ev - er

rall.

die; (shall ev - er die;) We shall sing the same old sto - ry, We shall

Where They Never Say "Good-bye."

wear a crown of glo-ry, In the land where they nev-er say good-bye..........
they nev-er say good-bye.

141   Silent Night! Holy Night!

Joseph Mohr.
M. 50 = ♩.

Franz Gruber.

1. Si - lent night! Ho - ly night! All is dark, save the light,
2. Si - lent night! Peace - ful night! Dark-ness flies, all is light;
3. Si - lent night! Ho - ly night! Guid - ing Star, lend thy light;
4. Si - lent night! Ho - li - est night! Wondrous Star, lend thy light;

Yon-der, where they sweet vig-ils keep, O'er the Babe who in si - lent sleep
Shep-herds hear the an - gels sing, "Al - le - lu - ia! hail the King!
See the East - ern wise men bring Gifts and hom - age to our King!
With the an - gels let us sing Al - le - lu - ia to our King!

Rests in heav - en - ly peace, Rests in heav - en - ly peace.
Christ the Sav - ior is born, Je - sus the Sav - ior is born."
Christ the Sav - ior is born, Je - sus the Sav - ior is born!
Christ the Sav - ior is born, Je - sus the Sav - ior is born!

142 He Whispers His Love to Me.

V. McC.

M. 104

Vivian McCown.

1. 'Tis so sweet just to know that a-long the way Je-sus walks by my
2. When He scat-ters the gifts from His boundless store, And His show-ers of
3. When my heart is so tempt-ed and sore-ly tried, It is then that I
4. Oh, His voice is so won-drous-ly sweet to me! There's no mu-sic on

side all the live-long day, And He knows when the shad-ows be-
bless-ing a-round me pour, Lest I hum-ble and grate-ful for-
know He is by my side, And I know He will give me the
earth has such mel-o-dy; There's no joy that can come to the

gin to low'r, And He whis-pers His love to me o'er and o'er.
get to be, Je-sus whis-pers His won-der-ful love to me.
vic-to-ry As He whis-pers His won-der-ful love to me.
hu-man heart Like the joy that His love ev-er doth im-part.

CHORUS.

He whispers His love to me,   He whispers His love to me;
His love to me,   His love to me;

Lest I should stray from Him a-way, He whis-pers His love to me.

143 To Look On His Face.

James Rowe.

B. D. Ackley.

1. Oh, how sweet is the tho't that sal - va-tion has brought, Which to mem-o - ry
2. How it com-forts my soul when the trouble-waves roll, And my heart has no
3. With the dear ones who wait at the beau-ti - ful gate, I am long-ing His

ev - er will cling; When my la-bors are done and the life crown is won,
car - ol to sing, Just to think that some day, at the end of the way,
prais-es to sing; But I long o'er and o'er and I long ev - er-more,

CHORUS.

I shall look on the face of my King!
I shall look on the face of my King! To look on the face of my
Just to look on the face of my King.

King! What rapt-ure the bliss it will bring! Noth-ing else there will be

which will sat - is - fy me, But to look on the face of my King.

144 Columbia's Song.

Mrs. Frank A. Breck.   Chas. H. Gabriel

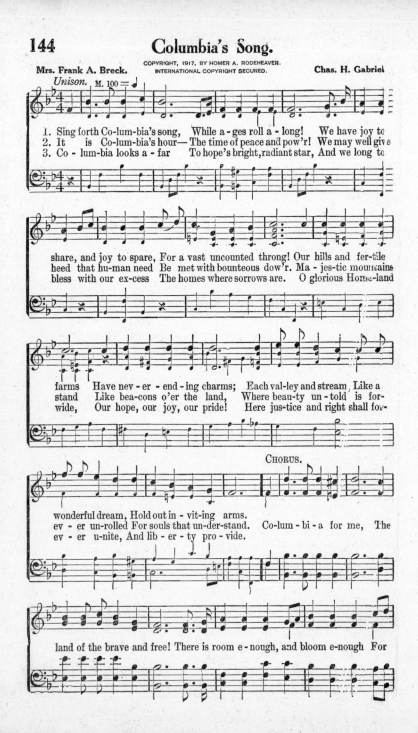

Unison. M. 100 = ♩

1. Sing forth Co-lum-bia's song,   While a-ges roll a-long!   We have joy to
2. It   is Co-lum-bia's hour— The time of peace and pow'r! We may well give
3. Co - lum-bia looks a-far   To hope's bright, radiant star, And we long to

share, and joy to spare, For a vast uncounted throng! Our hills and fer-tile
heed that hu-man need Be met with bounteous dow'r. Ma - jes-tic mountains
bless with our ex-cess The homes where sorrows are.   O glorious Home-land

farms   Have nev - er - end - ing charms;   Each val-ley and stream, Like a
stand   Like bea-cons o'er the land,   Where beau-ty un-told is for-
wide,   Our hope, our joy, our pride!   Here jus-tice and right shall for-

CHORUS.

wonderful dream, Hold out in - vit-ing arms.
ev - er un-rolled For souls that un-der-stand.   Co-lum - bi - a for me,   The
ev - er u-nite, And lib - er - ty pro - vide.

land of the brave and free! There is room e - nough, and bloom e-nough For

Columbia's Song.

mil-lions yet to be. Co-lum-bi- a, land of plen-ty, Of fruit, and wheat, and

corn! 'Tis a land of trees and balm-y breeze, Where freedom first was born.

145

Calvary.

Rev. A. H. Ackley.
DUET.

B. D. Ackley.

1. The ag - o - nies of Cal - va - ry, Could not His love dis-may;
2. He stood con-demned in Pilate's Hall, He heard the rab-bles' cry;
3. Lo! Je - sus stands with brok-en heart, With nail-pierced hands and feet;
4. The Sav - ior stands at thy heart's door Bruised for thy cru - el sin;

He would not yield, tho' God re-vealed The price that He must pay.
The King with none to own His cause, My cause would not de - ny;
He points un - to His cross of woe, Where love and mer-cy meet.
O why not o - pen wide the door And let Him en - ter in?

He would not yield, tho' God re - vealed The price that He must pay.
The King with none to own His cause, My cause would not de - ny.
He points un - to His cross of woe, Where love and mer-cy meet.
O why not o - pen wide the door And let Him en - ter in?

146 Is it I? Is it You?

Mrs. C. H. M.

Mrs. C. H. Morris.

Effective as a Solo. M. 60

1. Some-one is turn-ing his back on the Sav-ior And thus cru-ci-
2. Just as of yore He on tri-al is stand-ing, De-nied by the
3. Some-one too late will for mer-cy be call-ing With death and e-
4. Some-one is cross-ing the dead-line, di-vid-ing The old life of

fy-ing the Mas-ter a-new, Some-one is slight-ing His par-don-ing
man-y and loved by the few; Some-one "A-way with Him!" still is de-
ter-ni-ty loom-ing in view, Cry-ing for mountains on him to be
sin and of shame from the new; Some-one just now is for Je-sus de-

fa-vor; My Lord, is it I?...... My friend, is it you?
mand-ing; My Lord, is it I?...... My friend, is it you?
fall-ing; My Lord, is it I?...... My friend, is it you?
cid-ing; My Lord, is it I?...... My friend, is it you?

CHORUS.

O who.... would the love of the Sav-ior a-buse, The mer - cy and
O who   The mer - cy

par-don He of-fers, re-fuse? The lost...... are so man-y, the
The lost

Is it I? Is it You?

rit.

saved are so few,—My Lord, is it I?.... My friend is it you?

147

Jesus Loves Even Me.

P. P. B.

COPYRIGHT, 1902, BY THE JOHN CHURCH COMPANY. USED BY PERMISSION.

P. P. Bliss.

M. 60 = ♩.

1. I am so glad that our Fa - ther in heav'n Tells of His love in the
2. Tho' I for-get Him and wan-der a - way, Still He doth love me wher-
3. Oh, if there's on - ly one song I can sing, When in His beau-ty I

Book He has giv'n; Won-der-ful things in the Bi - ble I see,
er I stray; Back to His dear lov - ing arms would I flee,
see the Great King, This shall my song in e - ter - ni - ty be:

CHORUS.

This is the dear-est, that Je - sus loves me.
When I re - mem-ber that Je - sus loves me. I am so glad that
"Oh, what a won-der that Je - sus loves me!"

1

Je-sus loves me, Je-sus loves me,

2

Je - sus loves me; e - ven me.

148 Keep On Believing.

Arrangement copyright, 1925, by Homer A. Rodeheaver.

C. S. B.
Duet for Sop. and Tenor, or Alto.

Adapted from C. S. Bullock,
by C. H. G.

1. When thou art weak-est, tri-als a - bound, Subtle temp-ta - tions,
2. If in temp - ta - tion, then He is near; He knows thy dan - ger,
3. If old com - pan-ions—friends of gone days— Gather a - round thee,

troubles sur - round, All things seem hopeless, nothing seems glad, All is de -
why shouldst thou fear? He will up-hold Thee, cause thee to stand, Cheering thee
temp to their ways, Look to the Sav - ior, seek Him in pray'r; Ho will pro-

CHORUS.

spair - ing, ev - en - time sad. Keep on be - liev - ing,
ev - er, hold-ing thy hand.
tect thee, nev - er de - spair. Keep on be - liev - ing,

Je - sus is near, ... Keep on be - liev- - ing, there's nothing to
Je - sus is near, Keep on believ - ing, there is

Keep On Believing.

fear;........ Keep on be - liev - ing, this is the
nothing to fear; Keep on be - liev - ing, For

way,........ Faith in the night as well as the day.
this is the way, Faith in the night as well as the day.

149 Step Out on the Promise.

Maggie Potter.
Arr. by E. E. F. M.

COPYRIGHT, 1894, BY E. F. MILLER.
BY PER.

E. F. Miller.

1. O mourn - er in Zi - on, how bless - ed art thou, For Je - sus is
2. Oh, ye that are hun-gry and thirst - y re - joice; For ye shall be
3. Who sighs for a heart from in - i - qui - ty free? Oh, poor troubled
4. The prom - ise can't save, tho' the prom - ise is true; 'Tis the blood we get

wait - ing to com - fort you now; Fear not to re - ly on the
filled; do you hear that sweet voice In - vit - ing you now to the
soul! there's a prom - ise for thee; There's rest, wea-ry one, in the
un - der, that cleans - es us through: It cleans - es me now, hal - le-

word of thy God, Step out on the prom - ise, get un-der the blood.
ban - quet of God? Step out on the prom - ise, get un-der the blood.
bos - om of God. Step out on the prom - ise, get un-der the blood.
lu - jah to God! Step out on the prom - ise, get un-der the blood.

150 Whispering Hope.

Arr. Copyrighted, 1924, by The Standard Pub. Co.

Alice Hawthorne.   Arr. by J. C. Blaker.

DUET.

1. Soft as the voice of an an - gel, Breathing a les-son un - heard,
2. If in the dusk of the twi - light, Dim be the region a · far,

Hope, with a gen-tle per - sua - sion, Whis-pers her comforting word.
Will not the deepen-ing dark - ness Bright-en the glimmering star?

Wait till the darkness is o - ver, Wait till the tempest is done,
Then when the night is up - on us, Why should the heart sink a-way?

Hope for the sunshine to-mor - row, Aft - er the shower is gone.
When the dark midnight is o - ver Watch for the breaking of day.

CHORUS.

Whis - - per-ing hope,.... Oh, how wel - come thy voice,....
Whispering hope, Whispering hope, Welcome thy voice, oh, how welcome thy voice,

Whispering Hope.

Mak - - ing my heart ... In its sor - - row re-joice.....

Making my heart, making my heart In its sorrow rejoice, re - joice.....

sorrow re-joice.

151   A Sinner Like Me.

C. J. B.   C. J. Butler.

Slow.

1. I was once far a - way from the Sav - ior, And as
2. I wan - der'd on in the dark - ness. Not a
3. And then, in that dark lone - ly hour,..

vile as a sin - ner could be; And I won-der'd if Christ the Re-
ray of light could I see; And the tho't fill'd my heart with
voice sweetly whis-pered to me, Saying, Christ the Re-deem-er has

A

rit.

deem - er Could save a poor sin - ner like me.
sad - ness, There's no hope for a sin - ner like me.
pow - er To save a poor sin - ner like me.

4 I listened: and lo! 'twas the Savior
   That was speaking so kindly to me;
I cried, "I'm the chief of sinners,
   Thou canst save a poor sinner like me!"

5 I then fully trusted in Jesus;
   And O, what a joy came to me!
My heart was filled with His praises
   For saving a sinner like me.

6 No longer in darkness I'm walking,
   For the light is now shining on me;
And now unto others I'm telling
   How He saved a poor sinner like me.

7 And when life's journey is over,
   And I the dear Savior shall see,
I'll praise Him forever and ever,
   For saving a sinner like me.

152 My Ain Countrie.

Mary Lee Demarest.

Scotch Air.

1. I am far frae my hame, an' I'm wear-y aft - en-whiles, For the
   An' I'll ne'er be fu' con-tent, un - til mine een do see The

D. C.— But these sights an' these soun's will as naething be to me, When I

langed-for hame-bringin', an' my Faither's welcome smiles }
gow-den gates o' heav-en [*Omit* ....] } an' my ain countrie.
hear the an-gels sing-in' [*Omit* ....] in my ain countrie.

{ The earth is fleck'd wi flow-ers, mon - y - tint - ed, fresh an' gay; }
{ The bird - ies war - ble blithe-ly, for my Fai-ther made them sae: }

2 I've His gude word o' promise that some gladsome day, the King
To His ain royal palace His banished hame will bring;
Wi' een an' wi' hert rinnin' owre, we shall see
The King in His beauty, in oor ain countrie.
My sins hae been mony, an' my sorrows hae been sair:
But there they'll never vex me, nor be remembered mair:
For His bluid has made me white, an' His han' shall dry my e'e,
When He brings me hame at last, to my ain countric.

3 He is faithfu', that hath promised, an' He'll surely come again,
He'll keep His tryst wi' me, at what oor I dinna ken;
But He bids me still to wait, an' ready aye to be,
To gang at ony moment to my ain countrie.
Sae i'm watching aye, and singin' o' my hame, as I wait,
For the soun'in' o' His fitfa' this side the gowden gate:
God gie His grace to ilka ane wha' listens noo to me,
That we a' may gang in gladness to oor ain countrie.

153 Have You Forgotten God?

C. H. G.

Chas. H. Gabriel.

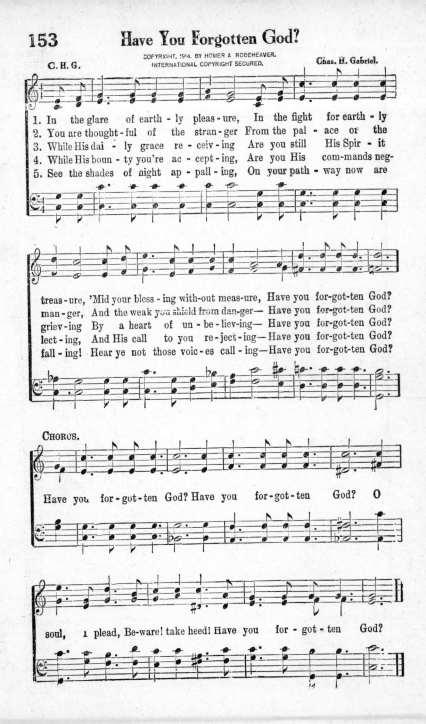

1. In the glare of earth-ly pleas-ure, In the fight for earth-ly treas-ure, 'Mid your bless-ing with-out meas-ure, Have you for-got-ten God?
2. You are thought-ful of the stran-ger From the pal-ace or the man-ger, And the weak you shield from dan-ger— Have you for-got-ten God?
3. While His dai-ly grace re-ceiv-ing Are you still His Spir-it griev-ing By a heart of un-be-liev-ing— Have you for-got-ten God?
4. While His boun-ty you're ac-cept-ing, Are you His com-mands neg-lect-ing, And His call to you re-ject-ing— Have you for-got-ten God?
5. See the shades of night ap-pall-ing, On your path-way now are fall-ing! Hear ye not those voic-es call-ing— Have you for-got-ten God?

CHORUS.

Have you for-got-ten God? Have you for-got-ten God? O soul, I plead, Be-ware! take heed! Have you for-got-ten God?

154 The Pearly-White City.

A. F. I.

Arthur F. Ingler.

Moderato.

1. There's a ho-ly and beau-ti-ful cit-y, Whose builder and ru-ler is God;
2. No sin is allow'd in that cit-y, And nothing de-fil-ing or mean;
3. No heartaches are known in that cit-y, No tears ev-er moisten the eye;
4. My loved ones are gathering yon-der, My friends are fast passing a-way;

John saw it descending from heaven, When Patmos in ex-ile, he trod,
No pain and no sickness can en-ter, No crape in that cit-y is seen;
There's no disappointment in heav-en, No en-vy or strife in the sky;
And soon I may join their bright number, And dwell in e-ter-ni-ty's day;

Its high, massive wall is of jas-per, The cit-y it-self is pure gold;
Earth's sorrows and cares are forgotten, No tempter is there to an-noy;
The saints are all sanc-ti-fied, whol-ly, They live in sweet harmony there;
They're safe now in glory with Je-sus, Their tri-als and battles are past;

rit. ad lib.

And when my frail tent here is folded, Mine eyes shall its glories be-hold.
No parting words ev-er are spo-ken, There's nothing to hurt and de-stroy.
My heart is now set on that cit-y, And some day its blessings I'll share.
They o-ver-came sin and the tempter, They've reached that fair cit-y at last.

CHORUS. *Slow*

In that bright cit-y, pearl-y-white cit-y, I have a

The Pearly-White City.

mau-sion, an harp and a crown; Now I am watch-ing, wait-ing and

rit. ad lib.

long-ing For the white cit - y.... John saw com-ing down.

155

How Could It Be?

Rev. N. A. McAuley.

Chas. H. Marsh.

Slowly.

1. Poor and de-spised He came seek-ing for me, Bear - ing my
2. Down in Geth-sem - a - ne, there I be - hold Je - sus in
3. See Him as-cend the mount, bleed-ing for me, Where thro' the
4. Then in the tomb He lay, sleep-ing for me, Till came the

woe and shame my soul to free; For me He suf - fered here,
ag - o - ny, sor - row un - told; Then at the trait - or's call,
crim - son fount, cleans-ing I see; For me He left His throne,
prom - ised day of vic - to - ry; He from the grave a - rose,

Shed oft the bit - ter tear, In love so pure and dear, How could it be?
He went to Pi - lot's hall, Bear-ing the sins of all, How could it be?
For me He did a-tone, Dy - ing in shame a - lone, How could it be?
He conquer'd all His foes, Then He in glo-ry rose, How could it be?

156 Closer to Jesus

R. H. McDaniel.

Chas. H. Gabriel.

M. 46 =

1. The Sav - ior is dear - er to me ev - 'ry day, The clo - ser I
2. His serv - ice grows sweet - er and sweet - er to me, The clo - ser I
3. His love more a - bund - ant - ly flows thro' my heart, The clo - ser I
4. I'm long - ing the more in His like - ness to be, The clo - ser I

live to Him; And bright - er His glo - ry il - lu - mines my way,
live to Him; And more of His good - ness and mer - cy I see,
live to Him; And rich - er the bless - ings that He doth im - part,
live to Him; And sur - er I am that His face I shall see,

CHORUS.

The clo - ser I live to Him. Clo - ser to Him, clo - ser to
Ev - er

Him, I want to live clo - ser to Je - sus; There's no one so
oh,

pre - cious, so faith - ful to me, And I want to live clo - ser to Him.

157   The Unclouded Day.

Words and melody by
Rev. J. K. Alwood.

1. O they tell me of a home far be - yond the skies, O they
2. O they tell me of a home where my friends have gone, O they
3. O they tell me of a King in His beau - ty there, And they
4. O they tell me that He smiles on His chil - dren there, And His

tell me of a home far a - way; O they tell me of a home
tell me of that land far a - way; Where the tree of life
tell me that mine eyes shall be hold, Where He sits on the throne
smile drives their sor - rows all a - way; And they tell me that no tears

D. S.—*O they tell me of a home*

FINE.

where no storm-clouds rise, O they tell me of an un-cloud - ed day.
in e - ter - nal bloom Sheds its fragrance thro' the un-cloud - ed day.
that is whit - er than snow, In the cit - y that is made of gold.
ev - er come a - gain, In that love - ly land of un-cloud - ed day.

where no storm-clouds rise, O they tell me of an un-cloud-ed day.

CHORUS.   D. S.

O the land of cloud-less day, O the land of an un-cloud-ed day;

Look In The Bible.

Inscribed to Miss Grace Saxe, Bible Teacher of the Sunday Party.

Susan R. Peck.   Chas. H. Gabriel.

1. There's a Savior who of-fers to free you from sin, Look in the Bi-ble for
2. There's a King who now offers a share in His throne, Look in the Bi-ble for
3. He is pa-tient-ly waiting, and asks for your heart, Look in the Bi-ble for

that! Who'll keep you from falling, the vic-t'ry to win, Look in the Bi-ble for
that! A King who will give you all things for your own, Look in the Bi-ble for
that! 'Tis only your will that can keep you a-part, Look in the Bi-ble for

that.   Nev - er a need that He will not sup-ply; All things are now
that.   Say, have you ev - er heard of - fer so great, Or dreamed of so
that.   Take all the rich-es it of-fers to you! Stop! Look ye and

read-y, no good He'll de-ny; You've on - ly to ask—He will answer your cry—
mar - vel-ous king - ly es-tate? Oh, haste to accept it—soul, how can you wait?
lis - ten, it's warn-ings are true! Oh, do not re-fuse what He wants you to do—

CHORUS.

Look in the Bi-ble for that.   Look in the Bi - ble with won-der a-

Look In the Bible.

bound-ing; Search all its pag - es with prom-ise re-sound - ing; On its sure

word all His con - fi-dence founding, God gives you the Bi - ble for that.

159 Where He Leads Me.

E. W. Blandly.   Arr.

1. I   can hear my Sav - ior call - ing,   I   can hear my Sav - ior call - ing,
2. I'll go with Him thro' the garden,   I'll go with Him thro' the garden,
3. I'll go with Him thro' the judgment,   I'll go with Him thro' the judgment,
4. He will give me grace and glo - ry,   He will give me grace and glo - ry,

Cho.-*Where He leads me I   will fol - low, Where He leads me I   will fol-low,*

ad lib.   D. C.

I   can hear my Sav - ior call - ing, "Take thy cross and fol-low, fol - low me."
I'll go with him thro' the garden,   I'll go with Him, with Him all the way.
I'll go with Him thro' the judgment, I'll go with Him, with Him all the way.
He will give me grace and glo - ry,   And go with me, with me all the way.

Where He leads me I   will fol-low,   I'll go with Him, with Him all the way.

160 At the Place of Prayer.

Avis M. Christiansen.   **Chas. H. Gabriel.**

M. 100 = ♩

1. When your cross seems heav - y, and the path-way steep, When the night grows
2. When the old - time pow - er seems for - ev - er gone, When the world for-
3. Je - sus waits to take you in His arms of love From the lone - ly

drear - y, and the shad - ows deep, There's a ref - uge o - pen, bless - ed
gets you as it rush - es on; When you fast are sink - ing in - to
val - ley to the heights a - bove; You will find sweet com - fort in His

ha - ven fair—There's a bless - ing wait - ing at the place of Prayer!
deep de - spair—There's a bless - ing wait - ing at the place of Prayer!
pres - ence there—There's a bless - ing wait - ing at the place of Prayer!

D. S.—There's a bless - ing wait - ing at the place of Prayer!

CHORUS.

There's a bless - ing wait-ing at the place of Prayer! There is balm for sor - row,

there is rest from care; There is per - fect peace and joy be - yond com - pare;

161 I'll Go Where You Want Me to Go.

Mary Brown.   **Carrie E. Rounsefell**

1. It may not be on the mountain height, Or o-ver the storm-y sea,
2. Per-haps to-day there are lov-ing words Which Je-sus would have me speak;
3. There's surely somewhere a low-ly place In earth's harvest fields so wide,

It may not be at the bat-tle's front My Lord will have need of me;
There may be now in the paths of sin Some wand'rer whom I should seek:
Where I may la-bor thro' life's short day For Je-sus, the Cru-ci-fied;

But if, by a still, small voice He calls To paths that I do not know,
O Sav-ior, if Thou wilt be my guide, Tho' dark and rug-ged the way,
So trust-ing my all to Thy ten-der care, And know-ing Thou lov-est me,

FINE.

I'll answer, dear Lord, with my hand in Thine, I'll go where you want me to go.
My voice shall ech-o the mes-sage sweet, I'll say what you want me to say.
I'll do Thy will with a heart sin-cere, I'll be what you want me to be.

D.S.—*I'll say what you want me to say, dear Lord, I'll be what you want me to be.*

REFRAIN.   D.S.

I'll go where you want me to go, dear Lord, Over mountain, or plain, or sea;

162 Elijah's God Still Lives.

Rev. W. G.

COPYRIGHT. 1902, BY W. GRUM,
HOMER A RODEHEAVER, OWNER.

Rev. W. Grum.

1. E - li - jah made a sac - ri - fice To of - fer to Je - ho - vah;
2. E - li - jah's God still lives to-day, And an-swers still by fire;
3. E - li - jah's God still lives to-day, And an-swers still in pow - er;

It had been wet with wa - ter thrice, Baal's sac - ri - fice was o - ver;
My friend, just let Him have His way, He'll grant your heart's de - sire,
As when E - li - jah pray'd for rain, God answer'd with a show - er;

E - li - jah pray'd, the fire came down, And lick'd the wa - ter all around,
Con - sume the sac - ri - fice you make And bid your slumb'ring soul awake,
If you would have your soul refresh'd With rain that falls from heav - en,

And doubting ones be-liev'd and found E - li - jah's God was liv - ing.
And chains of in - bred sin will break, E - li - jah's God is liv - ing.
You must pray thro' like all the rest, And show - ers shall be giv - en.

CHORUS.

E - li - jah's God still lives to - day, To take the guilt of sin a - way;

Elijah's God Still Lives.

And when I pray my heart's de-sire, Up-on my soul He sends down fire.

163 Secret Prayer.

C. H. G.

Chas. H. Gabriel.

Male Voices sing the melody.

M. 69 = ♩

1. Sweet se-cret prayer, com-fort di-vine, There, O my
2. Sweet se-cret prayer, com-fort di-vine, There do Thine
3. Sweet se-cret prayer, com-fort di-vine, There do I

Lord, I know Thou art mine; Great Mas-ter, there in
arms, Lord, round me en-twine; Riv-ers of love and
feel I tru-ly am Thine; Heav'n's win-dows o-pen,

se-cret with Thee,.... Heav-en comes near-er and near-er to me.
mer-cy there flow,.... Balm for all sor-row that mor-tal can know.
Je-sus is near,.... Near to my soul, and the Fa-ther will hear.

CHORUS.

Blessings attend and fol-low us there; Heaven comes nearer and nearer in prayer.

164   Jesus.

Ina Duley Ogdon.   **B. D. Ackley.**

Not too fast.

1. There is a name I love to hear, Je - sus, bless-ed Je - sus!
2. There is a pic - ture in my heart, Je - sus, bless-ed Je - sus!
3. There is a sa - cred mem - o - ry, Je - sus, bless-ed Je - sus!
4. There is a home in love di - vine, Je - sus, bless-ed Je - sus!

It falls like mu - sic on my ear, Je - sus, bless-ed Je - sus!
It makes the lov - ing tear-drops start, Je - sus, bless-ed Je - sus!
Of Beth - le - hem to Cal - va - ry, Je - sus, bless-ed Je - sus!
I am so glad that He is mine, Je - sus, bless-ed Je - sus!

CHORUS.

No oth - er is so dear to me, As Je - sus Lamb of Cal - va - ry,

His pre-cious life He gave for me, Je - sus, bless - ed Je - sus!

165 Memories of Mother.

Fred P. Morris.

Robert Harkness.

M. 69 = ♩.

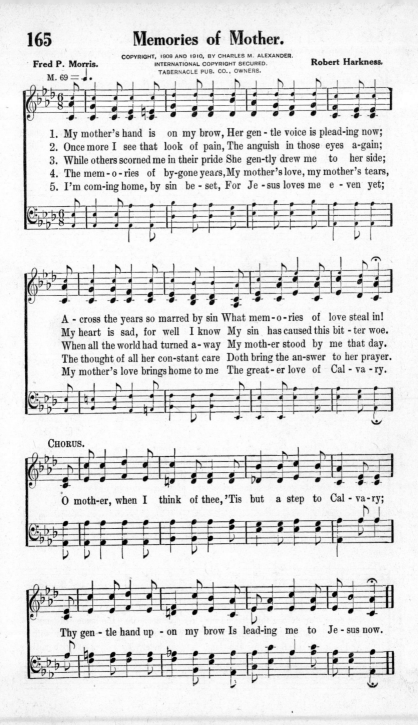

1. My mother's hand is on my brow, Her gen-tle voice is plead-ing now;
2. Once more I see that look of pain, The anguish in those eyes a-gain;
3. While others scorned me in their pride She gen-tly drew me to her side;
4. The mem-o-ries of by-gone years, My mother's love, my mother's tears,
5. I'm com-ing home, by sin be-set, For Je-sus loves me e-ven yet;

A-cross the years so marred by sin What mem-o-ries of love steal in!
My heart is sad, for well I know My sin has caused this bit-ter woe.
When all the world had turned a-way My moth-er stood by me that day.
The thought of all her con-stant care Doth bring the an-swer to her prayer.
My mother's love brings home to me The great-er love of Cal-va-ry.

CHORUS.

O moth-er, when I think of thee, 'Tis but a step to Cal-va-ry;

Thy gen-tle hand up-on my brow Is lead-ing me to Je-sus now.

166 The Old and New Home.

Old English.   Arranged by E. Bristow.

DUET

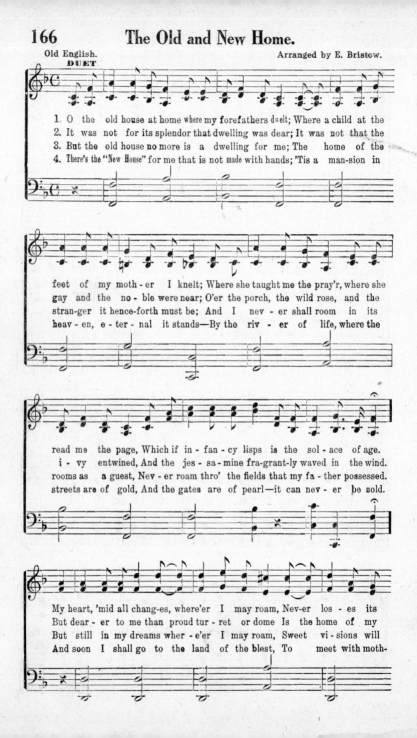

1. O the old house at home where my forefathers dwelt; Where a child at the
2. It was not for its splendor that dwelling was dear; It was not that the
3. But the old house no more is a dwelling for me; The home of the
4. There's the "New House" for me that is not made with hands; 'Tis a man-sion in

feet of my moth - er I knelt; Where she taught me the pray'r, where she
gay and the no - ble were near; O'er the porch, the wild rose, and the
stran-ger it hence-forth must be; And I nev - er shall room in its
heav - en, e - ter - nal it stands—By the riv - er of life, where the

read me the page, Which if in - fan - cy lisps is the sol - ace of age.
i - vy entwined, And the jes - sa - mine fra-grant-ly waved in the wind.
rooms as a guest, Nev - er roam thro' the fields that my fa - ther possessed.
streets are of gold, And the gates are of pearl—it can nev - er be sold.

My heart, 'mid all chang-es, where'er I may roam, Nev-er los - es its
But dear - er to me than proud tur - ret or dome Is the home of my
But still in my dreams wher - e'er I may roam, Sweet vi - sions will
And soon I shall go to the land of the blest, To meet with moth-

The Old and New Home.

love for   the   old house at home; For 'twas there at   the   feet   of   my
fa - ther, the   old house at home; For 'twas there at   the   feet   of   my
come of   the   old house at home; For 'twas there at   the   feet   of   my
er   and   the loved ones at rest; And 'tis there 'round a throne pearl - y

moth - er   I   knelt, In the   old house at home where my fore-fa-thers dwelt.
moth - er   I   knelt, In the   old house at home where my fore-fa-thers dwelt.
moth - er   I   knelt, In the   old house at home where my fore-fa-thers dwelt.
white we shall sing,   In that "New House at Home," 'tis the home of   a King!

CHORUS.

O the old house at home, O the old house at home,   My heart nev-er changes
O the old house at home, O the old house at home,   My heart nev-er changes
O the old house at home, O the old house at home,   My heart nev-er changes
O the new house at home, O the new house at home,   My soul now is long-ing

1-2-3.-for the   old house at home; er chang - es for the   old   house at home.
4.-for the   old house at home; is long - ing for the   new house at home.

167 The Stranger of Galilee.

COPYRIGHT, 1907, BY CHAS. H. GABRIEL.
The Standard Publishing Co., owners.

Mrs. C. H. M.

Mrs. C. H. Morris.

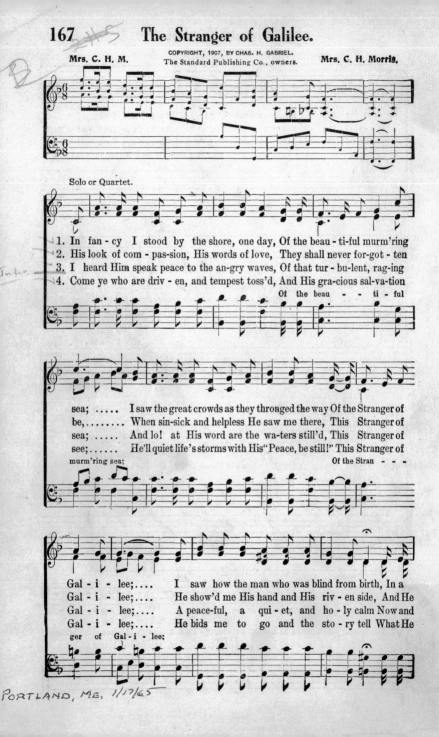

Solo or Quartet.

1. In fan - cy I stood by the shore, one day, Of the beau - ti-ful murm'ring
2. His look of com - pas-sion, His words of love, They shall never for-got - ten
3. I heard Him speak peace to the an-gry waves, Of that tur - bu-lent, rag-ing
4. Come ye who are driv - en, and tempest toss'd, And His gra-cious sal-va-tion

Of the beau - - ti-ful

sea; ..... I saw the great crowds as they thronged the way Of the Stranger of
be, ... When sin-sick and helpless He saw me there, This Stranger of
sea; ..... And lo! at His word are the wa-ters still'd, This Stranger of
see; ...... He'll quiet life's storms with His "Peace, be still!" This Stranger of

murm'ring sea; Of the Stran - - -

Gal - i - lee; .... I saw how the man who was blind from birth, In a
Gal - i - lee; .... He show'd me His hand and His riv - en side, And He
Gal - i - lee; .... A peace-ful, a qui - et, and ho - ly calm Now and
Gal - i - lee; .... He bids me to go and the sto - ry tell What He

ger of Gal - i - lee;

PORTLAND, ME. 1/17/65

The Stranger of Galilee.

mo-ment was made to see;...... The lame was made whole by the matchless skill
whispered "It was for thee!"... My bur-den fell off at the pierc-ed feet
ev - er a-bides with me;...... He hold-eth my life in His might-y hands,
ev - er to you will be,...... If on-ly you let him with you a-bide,
mo - - ment was made to see;

CHORUS.

Of the Stran-ger of Gal - i - lee.
Of the Stran-ger of Gal - i - lee. And I felt I could love Him for-
This Stran-ger of Gal - i - lee. *omit cho. between 2+3.*
This Stran-ger of Gal - i - lee. 4th v. Oh my friend won't you love Him for-

ff   p   rit.   tempo.

ev - - er,   So gra-cious and ten-der was He!.......... I
ev - - er,   So gra-cious and ten-der was He!.......... Ac-
ev - er and ev - er,   *he'll be* so ten-der is He!

cres.   *Last vs.*   rit. e dim.

claim'd Him that day as my Sav - - ior,   This Stranger of Gal - i - lee.
cept Him to-day as your Sav - - ior   This Stranger of Gal - i - lee.
Lord and my Sav-ior,

168   I Know.

W. H. O. and C. H. G.   Copyright, 1903, by E. O. Excell.   Chas. H. Gabriel.

1. You ask me how I gave my heart to Christ? O yes, I know! There
2. You ask me when I gave my heart to Christ? Yes, I can tell! The
3. You ask me where I gave my heart to Christ? Yes, I can say! That

came a yearn-ing in my soul for Him, So long a - go, I found earth's
day, and just the hour, in - deed, I now Re-mem-ber well; It was when
sa - cred place can nev - er fade from sight, As yes - ter-day; Per-haps He

fairest flow'rs would fade and die, I wept for something that would sat-is-
I was struggling all a - lone, The light of His for-giv-ing spir - it
tho't it bet-ter I should not For - get the place, for I should love the

fy, And in my grief, somehow, I seemed to dare To lift my
shone In-to my heart all cloud - ed o'er with sin, That I un-
spot, And un - til I be - hold Him face to face, 'Twill be to

brok - en heart to Him in pray'r. O yes, I know! And I can
locked the door and let Him in.
me, on earth, the dear - est place. O yes, I know! And I

I Know.

tell you how........ I know, I know He is my Sav-ior now.
can. tell you how
tell you when;...... I know, I know He in so dear since then.
can tell you when;
tell you where;...... I know, I know He came and blest me there.
can tell you where;

169

"Almost Persuaded."

P. P. B.

P. P. Bliss.

M. 152 =

1. "Al-most per-suad-ed" now to be-lieve; "Al-most per-suad-ed"
2. "Al-most per-suad-ed"—come, come to-day! "Al-most per-suad-ed"—
3. "Al-most per-suad-ed"—har-vest is past! "Al-most per-suad-ed"—

Christ to re-ceive; Seems now some soul to say: "Go, Spir-it,
turn not a-way! Je-sus in-vites you here, An-gels are
doom comes at last! "Al-most" can-not a-vail, "Al-most" is

go Thy way, Some more con-ven-ient day On Thee I'll call."
ling'ring near, Prayers rise from hearts so dear; O wan-derer, come!
but to fail; Sad, sad, that bit-ter wail: "Al-most—but lost!"

170 America the Beautiful.

Katharine Lee Bates.

Samuel A. Ward.

M. 100 = ♩

1. O beau - ti - ful for spa-cious skies, For am - ber waves of grain;....
2. O beau - ti - ful for pil - grim feet, Whose stern, im-pas-sioned stress....
3. O beau - ti - ful for he-roes proved In lib - er - at - ing strife,....
4. O beau - ti - ful for pa-triot dream That sees be - yond the years....

For pur - ple moun-tain maj - es - ties A - bove the fruit - ed plain!
A thor-ough-fare for free-dom beat A - cross the wil - der - ness!
Who more than self their coun-try loved, And mer - cy more than life!
Thine al - a - bas - ter cit - ies gleam Un-dimmed by hu - man tears!

A - mer - i - ca! A - mer - i - ca! God shed His grace on thee,
A - mer - i - ca! A - mer - i - ca! God mend thine ev - 'ry flaw,
A - mer - i - ca! A - mer - i - ca! May God thy gold re - fine
A - mer - i - ca! A - mer - i - ca! God shed His grace on thee,

And crown thy good with broth - er - hood From sea to shin - ing sea!
Con - firm thy soul in self - con-trol, Thy lib - er - ty in law!
Till all suc - cess be no - ble - ness, And ev - 'ry gain di - vine!
And crown thy good with broth - er - hood From sea to shin - ing sea!

171 Help Me to Wander No More.

Fanny J. Crosby.

B. D. Ackley.

M. 58 = ♩·

1. O Sav - ior, I come like the poor, wear-y dove, A ref-uge to find in the
2. I come to be cleansed in the fountain so free, The fountain of life Thou hast
3. O Sav - ior, I long for Thy glo - ry to live, I sigh for the peace that the
4. O Sav - ior divine, Thou hast answered my prayer; Now sweetly I rest from my

ark of Thy love; I know Thou art wait-ing my soul to re - store; O
o - pened for me; I know Thou art will-ing my soul to re - store; O
world can-not give; Thy grace and Thy Spir-it my soul can re - store; O
bur - den of care; My soul is up-lift - ed, my sor-row is o'er; O

CHORUS.

help me, I pray Thee, to wan - der no more. To wan-der no more, to

wan-der no more, Dear Sav-ior, I pray Thee, O help me to wander no more.

172 Where Is Thy Refuge?

Fanny J. Crosby.

Silas J. Vail.

1. Say, where is thy refuge, poor sin-ner, And what is thy prospect to-day?
2. The Master is calling thee, sin - ner, In tones of compassion and love,
3. As sum-mer is wan-ing, poor sin-ner, Re-pent, ere the sea-son is past;

Why toil for the wealth that will per-ish, The treasures that rust and de-cay?
To feel that sweet rapture of par-don, And lay up thy treasure a - bove;
God's goodness to thee is ex-tend - ed, As long as the day-beam shall last;

Oh! think of thy soul, that for-ev - er Must live on e - ter - ni-ty's shore,
Oh! kneel at the cross where He suffered, To ransom thy soul from the grave;
Then slight not the warning re-peat-ed With all the bright moments that roll,

When thou in the dust art for-got - ten, When pleasure can charm thee no more.
The arm of His mer-cy will hold thee, The arm that is might-y to save.
Nor say, when the harvest is end - ed, That no one hath cared for thy soul.

Where Is Thy Refuge?

CHORUS.

'Twill prof - it thee nothing, but fear - ful the cost, To gain the whole world

if thy soul should be lost! To gain the whole world if thy soul should be lost.

173   Jesus Bids Us Shine.

Reissue, 1922, by Chas. H. Gabriel.   Renewal,
Homer A. Rodeheaver, owner.

E. A. H.

M. 72 = d

Eva A. Higgins.

1. Je - sus bids us shine with a bright, bright light! Bright lit-tle gems in the
2. Je - sus bids us fol - low, where He may lead; All that He tells us we'll
3. Je - sus bids us love Him with all our heart; Oh, with His love may we

Fine.

Sav-ior's sight; Shin-ing for the Mas-ter with all our might, Shine, shine, shine.
try to heed; Scattering a - bout us the gos - pel seed, Shine, shine, shine.
nev - er part; But, while lit-tle children, for heav'n we'll start, Shine, shine, shine.

D. S.—Hear the Master's voice saying: "Shine for me!" Shine, shine, shine.

CHORUS.

Bright lit-tle jew - els we will be; Shining with a light that all can see;

174   Some Day.

Dr. Victor M. Staley.   Chas. H. Gabriel.

1. Some day 'twill all be o - ver—the toils and cares of life; Some
2. Some day I'll see the man-sions of heav-en's cit - y fair; Some
3. Some day I'll see the Sav - ior, and know Him, face to face; Some

day the world be vanquished With all this mortal strife; Some day, the jour-ney
day I'll greet with pleasure The dear ones waiting there; Some day, I'll hear the
day receive, unmeasured, The blessings of His grace; Some day He'll smile up-

end - ed, I'll lay my bur-den down; Some day, in realms su-per-nal Re-
voic - es Of God's an-gel - ic throng; Some day I'll join the cho-rus In
on me From that white throne a - bove; Some day I'll know the full-ness Of

CHORUS.

ceive, at last my crown. Some day,............ some hap-py day,..........
heav'n's immortal song.
His un - dy - ing love.   Some happy day,   some happy day,

Some Day.

The Lord will wipe all tears a-way, ... And I shall go to dwell with
all tears a-way,

Him, ... To dwell with Him .... some hap-py day.
to dwell with Him,   to dwell with Him   hap-py day.

175   Just As My Father Wills.

Harriet E. Jones.   Chas. H. Gabriel.

M. 120

1. Just as He wills,... so let it be,.... Whose hand shall mark my path for me,
2. Just as He wills,... who knoweth why.. Dark clouds sometimes must veil the sky,—
3. Just as He wills,... enough for me, ... The God I trust the end can see;

Just what I need.... His eye can see; Just as...... my Fa-ther wills.
He chastens but..... to pu-ri-fy; Just as...... my Fa-ther wills.
In weal or woe .... my song shall be:— Just as...... my Fa-ther wills.

176 The Sinner and the Song.

W. L. T.

WILL L. THOMPSON.

SOLO.

1. A sin-ner was wand'ring at e - ven-tide, His tempter was watching close
2. He stopp'd and listen'd to ev-'ry sweet chord, He re-membered the time he

by at his side; In his heart raged a battle for right against wrong, But hark! from the
once lov'd the Lord; Come on! says the tempter, come on with the throng; But hark! from the

QUARTET. *pp*

church he hears the sweet song: Je-sus, lov-er of my soul, Let me to Thy bosom fly,
church again swells the song: While the billows near me roll, While the tempest still is high.

SOLO.

O tempt-er, de - part, I have served thee too long; I fly to the Saviour, He

dwells in that song. O Lord, can it be that a sinner like me, May find a sweet refuge by

The Sinner and the Song—Concluded.

Quartet.

coming to Thee? Oth-er ref-uge have I none, Hangs my helpless soul on Thee.

Solo.   *Quartet.* pp

I come, Lord, I come, Thou'lt forgive the dark past, And Oh, receive my soul at last.

177   I Love Him.

London Hymn Book.   USED BY PER.   S. C. Foster.

1. Gone from my heart the world with all its charm; Gone are my sins and
2. Once I was lost up - on the plains of sin; Once was a slave to
3. Once I was bound, but now I am set free; Once I was blind, but

all that would a-larm; Gone ev - er-more, and by His grace I know The
doubts and fears within; Once was a - fraid to trust a lov - ing God, But
now the light I see; Once I was dead, but now in Christ I live, To

D. S. — *Be-cause He first loved me, And*

FINE. CHORUS.   D. S.

pre-cious blood of Je-sus cleanses white as snow.
now my guilt is washed a-way in Je - sus' blood. I love Him, I love Him,
tell the world the peace that He alone can give.

purchased my sal - va - tion On Calv'ry's tree.

Mother Knows.

Solo and Duet.

FROM WHITE RIBBON VIBRATIONS BY PER. ENGLEWOOD, COLO.
COPYRIGHT, 1890, BY FLORA H. CASSEL.

Anon.

Flora Hamilton Cassel.

1. No-bod-y knows of the work it makes To keep the home to-geth-er,
2. No-bod-y knows of the sleep-less care Bestowed on ba - by broth-er,
3. No-bod-y knows of the anxious fears, Lest darlings may not weath-er,
4. No-bod-y clings to the wayward child, Tho' scorn'd by ev - 'ry oth-er,

No-bod-y knows of the steps it takes, No-bod-y knows but moth-er;
No-bod-y knows of the tend-er pray'r, No-bod-y knows but moth-er;
Storms of this life in the com-ing years, No-bod-y knows but moth-er;
Leads it so gen-tly from path-ways wild, No-bod-y can but moth-er;

No-bod-y list-ens to child-ish woes, Which kiss-es on-ly smoth-er,
No-bod-y knows of the lessons taught, Of lov-ing one an - oth - er;
No-bod-y knows of the tears that start, The grief she glad-ly smoth-er,
No-bod-y knows of the hour-ly pray'r, For him, our err-ing broth-er,

No-bod-y's pain'd by the might-y blow, No-bod-y,—on-ly moth-er.
No-bod-y knows of the patience sought, No-bod-y,—on-ly moth-er.
No-bod-y knows of the break-ing heart, No-bod-y,—on-ly moth-er.
Pride of her heart, once so pure and fair, No-bod-y,—on-ly moth-er.

No Longer Lonely.

179

Robert Harkness.

R. H.

1. On life's pathway I am nev-er lone-ly, My Lord is with me, my Lord di-
2. I shall not be lone-ly in my sor-row, He will sus-tain me un-til the
3. I shall not be lone-ly in the val-ley, Tho' shadows gath-er, I will not

vine, Ev-er pres-ent Guide, I trust Him on-ly, No lon-ger
end; Dark-est night He turns to bright-est mor-row, No lon-ger
fear; He has prom-ised ev-er to up-hold me, No lon-ger

Chorus.

lone-ly, for He is mine.... No longer lone-ly, No longer lone-ly, For
lone-ly, He is my Friend.... No longer lone-ly, No longer lone-ly, For
lone-ly, He will be near.....

Je-sus is the Friend of friends to me;..... No longer lone-ly, No lon-ger
to me;

lone-ly, For Je-sus is the Friend of friends to me.
of friends to me.

The Model Church.

May be used as a reading with instrumental accompaniment.

John Yates.   Arranged for this book,

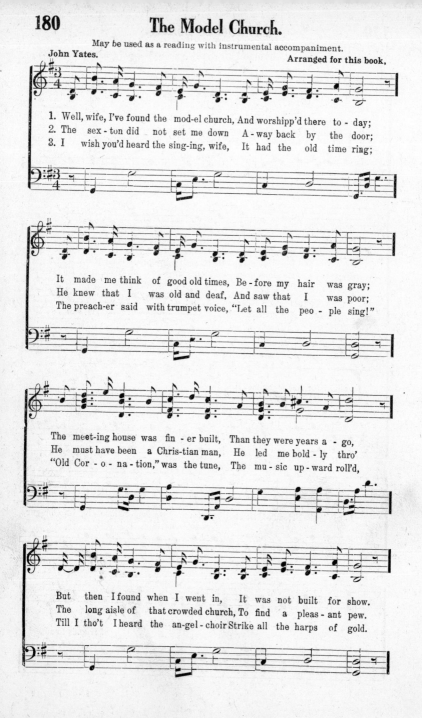

1. Well, wife, I've found the mod-el church, And worshipp'd there to - day;
2. The sex - ton did not set me down A - way back by the door;
3. I wish you'd heard the sing-ing, wife, It had the old time ring;

It made me think of good old times, Be - fore my hair was gray;
He knew that I was old and deaf, And saw that I was poor;
The preach-er said with trumpet voice, "Let all the peo - ple sing!"

The meet-ing house was fin - er built, Than they were years a - go,
He must have been a Chris-tian man, He led me bold - ly thro'
"Old Cor - o - na-tion," was the tune, The mu - sic up - ward roll'd,

But then I found when I went in, It was not built for show.
The long aisle of that crowded church, To find a pleas - ant pew.
Till I tho't I heard the an-gel - choir Strike all the harps of gold.

The Model Church.

4 My deafness seemed to melt away,
My spirit caught the fire;
I joined my feeble trembling voice
With that melodious choir;
And sang, as in my youthful days,
"Let angels prostrate fall;

Bring forth the roy - al di - a - dem, And crown Him Lord of all."

5 I tell you, wife, it did me good
To sing that hymn once more;
I felt like some wrecked mariner
Who gets a glimpse of shore.
I almost want to lay aside
This weather-beaten form,
And anchor in the blessed port,
Forever from the storm.

6 'Twas not a flowery sermon, wife,
But simple gospel truth;
It fitted humble men like me;
It suited hopeful youth.

To win immortal souls to Christ,
The earnest preacher tried;
He talked not of himself, or creed,
But Jesus crucified.

7 Dear wife, the toil will soon be o'er,
The victory soon be won;
The shining land is just ahead,
Our race is nearly run;
We're nearing Canaan's happy shore,
Our home so bright and fair;
Thank God, we'll never sin again;

There'll be no sor - row there; There'll be no sor - row there: In

heaven a - bove where all is love, There'll be no sor - row there.

181 A Story of Love.

C. H. G.

Chas. H. Gabriel.

M. 60 = ♩.

1. Sweet and clear on my ear Voi - ces are fall - ing from far a - way,
2. From a - far shines a star Seem - ing to speak to my long - ing heart;
3. Light - ly tread where the dead Slum - ber while e - ons of time go by;

Like the gleam of a dream, Lur - ing and lead - ing me day by day.
Fain would I give re - ply, And in the se - cret would have a part.
Si - lent - ly, rev - 'rent - ly, While thro' the for - ests the night - winds sigh.

Soft and low, to and fro, Swell - ing with mel - o - dy from a - bove
Shadows creep, long and deep, And thro' the gloaming the breez - es blow,
Look and see! 'tis for thee Stand - eth a cross in the fad - ing light!

As they roll o'er my soul, Tell - ing their sto - ry of love......
While I wait, long and late, List'ning for that I would know......
Hark! that sigh—and the cry Borne on the bos - om of night......

Sostenuto.

Star - ry eyes bright, shin - ing at night, Watch - ing a - far with your
Beau - ti - ful moon, fair - er than noon, Grant, I be - seech of thee,
Hid - ing his light, that he thus might Cov - er Gol - go - tha from

A Story of Love.

sil - v'ry light,   Sail - ing on wings,   see - ing all things,   Hear - ing the
this one boon:—   Did your soft rays   kiss His kind face   As   He looked
heaven's sight,   Sorrowed the sun   o - ver the One   Who for the

song all   cre - a - tion sings;   Whis - per it low,   for I would know,
up,   in that lone - ly place?   As He knelt there   fer - vent in prayer,
world a   sal - va - tion won.   Low - ly He came,   died He in shame—

Tho' it was such a long time a - go—   Who did you see   pray-ing for me
Did not an an - gel His sor-row share?   Pray-ing for me!   Yes, it was He,
Died for the sin - ner, O praise His name!   Now I can see,   pray-ing for me,

Deep   in the shade of Geth-sem - a - ne?   Ten - der - ly
Je - sus, my Sav - ior, of Gal - i - lee!
Christ, my Re-deem - er, of Cal - va - ry.   Ten - der - ly, sweet - ly the

now   they roll,   Like   a   song   to   my soul.
ca - den - ces roll, Like a   song in the night to   my   soul............

182 Wonderful Love.

C. H. G.   COPYRIGHT, 1929, RENEWAL, HOMER A. RODEHEAVER, OWNER   Chas. H. Gabriel.

1. I think, when I read the sweet sto - ry, How Je - sus came
2. And when I am foll'wing His foot - steps, New vi - sions of
3. Tho' ha - ted, de - spised, and re - ject - ed, Neg - lect - ed a -

down from His throne, To res - cue the per - ish-ing sin - ner, To
beau-ty un - fold, Till, lost in the depths of a - maze-ment, I
gain and a - gain, He nev - er de - serts nor for-sakes me, No

suf - fer and die for His own,.... Why should He as - sume my ob -
mar - vel such love to be - hold.... Why should He re - lin - quish His
mat - ter how way-ward I've been.... My bur - den of sor - row He

la - tion? Why should He thus purchase sal - va - tion? Such love is di -
glo - ry? Be - fore Him stood Cal - va - ry go - ry! Yet heaven re -
shar - eth, My stripes of in - iq - ui - ty wear - eth, My soul in His

vine re - ve - la - tion, Un - bounded, un-meas-ured, un - known...
sounds with the sto - ry Of love that can nev - er be told......
bo - som He bear - eth This won - der - ful Sav - ior of men.....

Wonderful Love.

CHORUS.

O it is won-der-ful that He should love me, And for my sins with His

life-blood a tone! Oh, it is won-der-ful, won-der-ful, won-der-ful!

Yet to the world be it known, He brought me a-gain to His own.

rit.

183 Holy Ghost, With Light Divine.

A. Reed.   Gottschalk.

M. 96 = ♩

1. Ho - ly Ghost, with light di - vine, Shine up - on this heart of mine;
2. Ho - ly Ghost, with pow'r di - vine, Cleanse this guilt-y heart of mine;
3. Ho - ly Ghost, with joy di - vine, Cheer this saddened heart of mine;
4. Ho - ly Spir - it, all di - vine, Dwell with - in this heart of mine;

Chase the shades of night a - way, Turn my dark-ness in - to day.
Long hath sin with-out con - trol, Held do - min - ion o'er my soul.
Bid my man - y sins de - part, Heal my wounded, bleeding heart.
Cast down ev - 'ry i - dol throne, Reign su-preme—and reign a-lone.

184 His Way With Thee.

C. S. N.

Rev. Cyrus S. Nusbaum.

1. Would you live for Je-sus and be al-ways pure and good? Would you walk with
2. Would you have Him make you free, and fol-low at His call? Would you know the
3. Would you in His kingdom find a place of constant rest? Would you prove Him

Him with-in the nar-row road? Would you have Him bear your bur-den,
peace that comes by giv-ing all? Would you have Him save you, so that
true each prov-i-den-tial test? Would you in His ser-vice la-bor

CHORUS.

car-ry all your load? Let Him have His way with thee.
you need nev-er fall? Let Him have His way with thee. His pow'r can make you
al-ways at your best? Let Him have His way with thee.

what you ought to be; His blood can cleanse your heart and make you free; His love can

rit.

fill your soul, and you will see 'Twas best for Him to have His way with thee.

Index

Titles in light face type are SOLOS. Titles in black face type are DUETS, some of which, however, may also be used as SOLOS.

Topical Index